The
Life
of the
Pond

Developed jointly with
The World Book Encyclopedia

Produced with the cooperation of
The United States Department of the Interior

OUR LIVING WORLD OF NATURE

The Life of the Pond

WILLIAM H. AMOS

Published in cooperation with
The World Book Encyclopedia

McGraw-Hill Book Company
NEW YORK   TORONTO   LONDON

WILLIAM H. AMOS *was raised in the Orient, where he first was introduced to aquatic and marine life in the Philippine Islands and in Japan. He has been associated with the New York Zoological Society, the Mt. Desert Biological Laboratory, and a number of marine laboratories in the United States and abroad, and he was a member of the Smithsonian-Bredin Expedition to the Lesser Antilles a few years ago. Mr. Amos is Chairman of the Science Department of St. Andrew's School in Middletown, Delaware, and is a Research Associate of the University of Delaware, Department of Biological Sciences. He has been a Senior Visiting Investigator at the Systematics-Ecology Program at the Marine Biological Laboratory in Woods Hole, Massachusetts, where he also serves as a consultant in biophotography. His work in fresh-water science, or limnology, commenced at Rutgers University and has continued during most of his professional life. Mr. Amos's present laboratory is on the shore of a highly productive pond, which he has studied for twenty years. His other major interests involve marine organisms and those of coastal estuaries. He is the author of many articles and books on marine and aquatic biology, most of which have been illustrated with his own biophotographs.*

Library of Congress Catalog Card Number: 67–16306

1234567890 NR 721069876

01586

OUR LIVING WORLD OF NATURE

Science Editor

RICHARD B. FISCHER   *Cornell University*

Board of Consultants

ROLAND CLEMENT   *National Audubon Society*
C. GORDON FREDINE   *National Park Service, The United States Department of the Interior*
WILLIAM H. NAULT   *Field Enterprises Educational Corporation*
BENJAMIN NICHOLS   *Cornell University*
EUGENE P. ODUM   *University of Georgia*
HENRY J. OOSTING   *Duke University*
OLIN SEWALL PETTINGILL, JR.   *Cornell University*
DAVID PIMENTEL   *Cornell University*
PAUL B. SEARS   *Yale University*
ROBERT L. USINGER   *University of California*

Readability Consultant

JOSEPHINE PIEKARZ IVES   *New York University*

Special Consultants for The Life of the Pond

DALE F. BRAY   *University of Colorado*
EDWIN T. MOUL   *Rutgers University*
ROBERT W. PENNAK   *University of Colorado*

Contents

WORLDS WITHIN WORLDS

APPENDIX

The Pond World

Beneath the surface of the water the light fades rapidly, changing from a sparkling gold to a dim yellowish brown. A dark and shadowed bottom is not far below. Thin light-colored stems bearing long, slender leaves rise to the surface from the soft mud. Out of their tangled mass emerges a swarm of small silvery fish with broad black bands running along their sides. Suddenly, from beneath a submerged leaf where it has been poised, a large insect with long pointed legs grasps one of the fish, which struggles convulsively and then is still.

Reaching out with waving tentacles from the stems are very small translucent animals, some colorless, some green. Along the surface of the bottom mud, multitudes of red worms extend out of their tubes. Strange creatures with sprawling legs and hinged, expansible jaws creep across the bottom.

On a smaller scale, minute shrimplike animals swim through the water with quick, erratic movements. But even they are among the larger creatures of a drifting, floating population; vast numbers of far smaller living things also dart and tumble through this watery world.

Where is this? Not in the ocean, not even in a large lake, but in a small pond overlooked by the thousands of motorists who pass it every day. The pond itself is less than an acre in extent and is no more than five feet deep in the center, yet it harbors a concentration of life far exceeding that of any lake and rivaling that of a tropical coral reef. A few miles away there is another pond about the same size; yet the plants and animals that it contains are different from those in this pond. No two ponds are exactly the same.

What is a pond?

Even experts find no convenient way of distinguishing a pond from a lake, or a bog from a pond, except in very general terms. If we attempt to define a pond in terms of a single characteristic, we run into trouble. For example, we might say that a body of water is a pond when it is shallow enough for rooted plants to reach the surface anywhere within its entire area. Yet we find that this definition is not entirely adequate.

There are many relatively small, shallow bodies of water in which few plants rise to the surface, yet surely these should be called ponds. Then there are very large bodies of shallow water, often found in swamps, that are full of rooted plants rising to the surface. But they cover many square miles and certainly cannot be called ponds.

The United States boasts over a million and a half ponds—small, relatively shallow bodies of water, each a self-contained miniature world harboring its own distinctive population of plant and animal life. No two ponds are ever quite alike, and no one pond remains the same for very long.

We might define a pond in terms not only of its depth but of its area and say that it is a body of water so small that its banks are not eroded by waves. (A large lake, by contrast, can produce sizable waves that wash out soil and eventually wear down rocks.) But not all small bodies of water are shallow. In the mountains it is possible to find quite small bodies of water that are very deep and therefore cannot be considered true ponds.

One distinguishing characteristic of a pond may be the relatively uniform temperature of the water. During summer, the water in a deep lake is divided into two distinct layers, the warm upper water and the cold deeper water. In a pond's shallow water there is little, if any, summer temperature layering; the change in temperature from top to bottom is gradual, not abrupt, and seldom amounts to more than ten degrees.

Perhaps if we combine all these ideas and agree that a pond is a shallow, rather small body of standing water with a uniform temperature throughout, give or take a few degrees, then we will have set limits that would exclude a lake, a river, a swamp, or a mountain stream. But there we must stop, for within even a small area of the country it is possible to find a bewildering variety of ponds, each with its own characteristics and its own population of plants and animals.

Why then should a book be written about ponds, if they are so small and so varied? Because a conservative estimate tells us that there are at least one and one-half million ponds

PONDS AND OUR NATIONAL PARKS

The Department of the Interior's National Park Service maintains a splendid system of parks, monuments, and recreational areas which include thousands and thousands of ponds that are usually overshadowed by more spectacular scenic attractions. Grand Teton National Park (*right*), for example, is best known for its rugged, soaring mountain peaks, yet within its boundaries are hundreds of ponds along the shores of which you can see and enjoy many of the plants and animals described in this book.

An alligator rests in the plant-tangled shallows of a pond in Florida's Everglades National Park (top left). Buffalo graze near a pond in Montana's National Bison Range (bottom), which is not part of the National Park System but rather a wildlife refuge administered by the Fish and Wildlife Service of the Department of the Interior.

in the United States, and that these might total as much as two million acres of water! Suddenly it becomes apparent that ponds compose a major aquatic habitat on our continent, and one that is exciting to study.

What is the history of your pond?

When you begin to study ponds, it is best to choose one small body of water and learn all you can about it. Such a concentrated approach is far better than skipping from pond to pond, stopping to look only at what is obvious, and never staying long enough to understand the complex community each one harbors.

First, you will want to know the physical nature of the pond—how large and how deep it is, how acid or alkaline the water is, and what the average water temperature is in

This horseshoe-shaped pond was created when an "oxbow" in a small, meandering river was by-passed by the main stream and thus was transformed into a body of standing water. Such ponds are most common where rivers flow through flat, level valleys.

the different seasons. You should also take into account its geographical location, that is, its latitude and its altitude above sea level. All these factors affect a pond and its life.

Then you will want to find out the history of your pond. It is valuable to know something of the geology of the land around it, how the pond originated, and how long it has been in existence. There are several types of natural ponds, although in the United States natural ponds are no longer nearly so numerous as those built by man. In the mountains, landslides may fill stream beds with earth and rock, causing ponds to form. Erosion usually tends to destroy lakes and ponds, but sometimes it creates depressions that fill with water. In lowland river valleys, streams twist back upon themselves, forming *meanders*. If a meander loops too much, the river may eventually by-pass it. The isolated U-shaped body of water that results is known as an oxbow lake, but it is really a kind of pond, for it is usually shallow and quickly fills with aquatic vegetation.

Dune ponds, such as this one on Cape Cod, form where winds scoop out the sand of an ocean beach or lake shore and heap it in barrier dunes. Even though such a pond may be but a few hundred yards away from the ocean, its water may be perfectly fresh.

Natural ponds often form near the deltas of rivers when silt deposits become high enough to dam off parts of the stream. They may also form behind barrier dunes on ocean beaches; the water contained here is as fresh as that farther inland and is not affected by the salt water just a few hundred yards away. Still another kind of natural pond may develop in cavities in limestone called *sinkholes* or *solution basins*. Some ponds are the last watery vestiges of what once were large lakes.

Glacial ponds, potholes, and kettles were once the most numerous, but now by far the greatest number of ponds are the result of man's activities, either planned or accidental. They may be ditches or canals, small reservoirs, millponds, quarry ponds, fishponds, or watering holes for cattle. Man-made ponds are used to supply water for irrigation, for fire protection, and for ice production. They may also be used to attract wild waterfowl, to control erosion, or to provide an area for recreation. Once established, each of these ponds will support a wide variety of life, both plant and animal.

Then, of course, there are also beaver ponds. Beavers have been constructing dams far longer than men have, and there is evidence that their ponds existed on this continent long before the dawn of recorded history.

In the United States today, man-made ponds outnumber those created by nature. This farm pond, bulldozed out of a pasture, serves a variety of purposes: livestock drink from it; it acts as a reservoir that can be tapped for irrigation or fire fighting; it affords human recreation in the form of swimming, fishing, and skating.

NATURE'S MASTER POND ENGINEERS

Man's closest rival in his ability to alter his surroundings is the beaver. This big rodent requires a pond in which it can build its home and store its winter food—and where no pond exists, the beaver is well equipped to construct one by damming the waters of a stream.

The beaver's construction materials include timber, rocks, mud, and grasses; its most important tools are its chisellike front teeth, which can bring down a six-inch-thick tree in ten minutes. Guided by inherited behavior patterns that might easily be mistaken for a reasoning intelligence, a colony of beavers—usually no more than a dozen animals—can build and maintain a remarkably well engineered dam, often impounding dozens of acres of water. Beaver dams average about seventy-five feet in length, but many are much longer. (The record appears to be a prodigious New Hampshire dam three-quarters of a mile long, the joint effort of a number of beaver colonies.)

Beaver ponds such as this were once a common sight throughout nearly the whole of the North American continent, but trappers, in quest of the animal's highly prized pelt, nearly drove the beaver into extinction. Protective legislation was enacted in time to save the beaver, and the creature has made a strong comeback over much of its original range.

17

Within the pond formed by the dam, the beaver colony builds its islandlike lodge of sticks and mud and stores cut and cured saplings, the bark of which will form the colony's principal winter food supply. As nearby food trees are depleted, the beavers may enlarge the dam to extend the pond margin to more distant stands of timber. Eventually, however, the colony must move on to a new location, and the abandoned pond gradually fills with silt and is transformed into rich meadowland, which in turn gives way to forest. Through this process, geologists believe, the unconscious efforts of thousands of generations of beavers produced the deep-soiled, fertile valleys that awaited the axes and plows of North America's first white settlers.

The beaver is well adapted for life in the water: its ear openings and nostrils are closed by valves when it submerges; special transparent eyelids cover its eyes underwater; the dense, oily fur protects it against the near-freezing waters of the pond in winter. The largest of our native rodents, a full-grown beaver can top seventy pounds.

A pond's many habitats

It is impossible to predict what species of animals and plants will be found in a given pond, but different sorts of organisms survive successfully in each of the particular habitats that exist there. In the *littoral*, or shore zone, there are various kinds of plants arranged according to their tolerance for the depth and movements of the water. In this area also live animals that do not exist successfully elsewhere. The surface film, too, supports its own plant and animal life, the *neuston*. The bottom has its characteristic flora and fauna, the *benthos*. And the *limnetic zone*, the open water away from the shore, contains motile forms, the strongly swimming fish and turtles (*nekton*) and the very small drifting animals and plants known as *plankton*.

Even the most casual observation reveals that the plank-

ton, nekton, and organisms of the littoral, surface film, and bottom do not live isolated lives. Herons and kingfishers catch fish in shallow water, bottom insects crawl up aquatic stems, snails rasp away at algal coatings on rooted aquatic plants, small crustaceans feed upon planktonic plants, fish seize and eat aquatic insect larvae, worms in the bottom extract organic matter from the mud, and many one-celled animals remove bacteria and algae suspended in the water. Everywhere the plants, large and small, grow profusely. The abundance of life is obvious, but the ways in which the pond's organisms depend upon one another for food, shelter, and reproduction are not so obvious.

To appreciate the remarkable community of plants and animals present in a pond, you must be familiar with some of the principles governing relationships between living things and their environment.

Plants are food factories

All life depends on a continuous inflow of energy. The substance of a plant or animal, or of ourselves, is held together, grown, repaired, and put into motion by means of energy derived from food. But food is manufactured only by green plants and some bacteria. When sunlight strikes a green plant growing on land or in water, remarkable events occur. In a process called *photosynthesis*, the energy of light is locked into a complex molecule never found by itself in the nonliving world. This molecule, a sugar, forms the basis of most foods used by both plants and animals for their growth and activity.

Plants carry on photosynthesis in their green pigment, *chlorophyll*, which is arranged in disklike layers within small oval bodies known as *chloroplasts*. Each cell in a green leaf has from several dozen to several hundred chloroplasts. For photosynthesis to occur, the plant must be exposed to sunlight, and it must have available to it both water and carbon dioxide. Aquatic plants have no difficulty in obtaining either. They are surrounded by water; and carbon dioxide, either from the atmosphere or from aquatic organisms that release it, dissolves readily in water. The minerals that plants need are also plentiful in the water of most ponds. Some aquatic plants absorb them through their roots or through their stems. Plants without roots or stems absorb them directly into their tissues.

The manufacture of living substances by photosynthetic plants, or *producers*, is known as *primary production*. When animals eat plants, or one another, they obtain the necessary nourishment to grow and make more of their own kind.

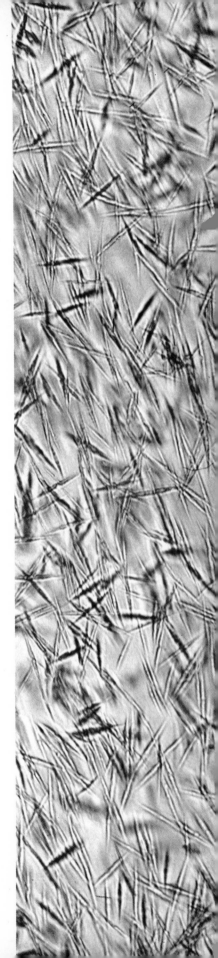

Cattails and water lilies (*left*) are both conspicuous members of the pond's plant population, but they are of less fundamental importance to the total food production of the pond than the drifting one-celled plants of the phytoplankton, such as desmids (*right*, magnified three hundred times). The phytoplankton can be compared to the grass of the dry land: these tiny green plants form the basic foodstuff of the pond world, upon which nearly all the pond's animals, large and small, are directly or indirectly dependent for sustenance. By contrast, only relatively few animals feed upon the larger plants.

23

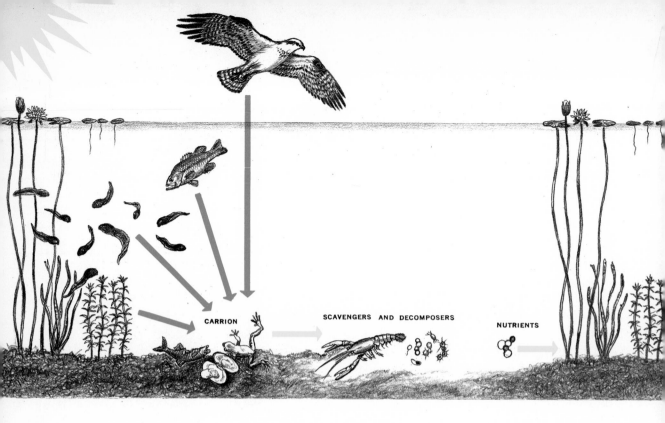

CARRION SCAVENGERS AND DECOMPOSERS NUTRIENTS

The common need for nourishment links all members of the pond community in a web of interrelationships shown in highly simplified form in the diagram above. The green plants—both the large ones like the water lilies and the minute ones that make up the algae—are the pond's *producers*, organisms capable of utilizing the sun's energy to convert simple, nonliving substances into living tissue. Organisms that feed directly on the plants are *first-order consumers*, represented here by the tadpoles. Bass—*second-order consumers*—prey upon tadpoles; ospreys—*third-order consumers*—prey upon bass. All these plants and animals eventually die and are reduced to simpler substances by the *decomposers* and the *scavengers*. After further bacterial processing, these substances are again made available to the green plants, completing the pond's food cycle.

Consumers and decomposers

Animals that feed directly on plants are called *first-order consumers*; those that capture and devour other animals are called *second-* or *third-order consumers*, depending upon how many steps removed they are from the plant producers. Among first-order consumers, there are animal plankton, which feeds upon plant plankton, and larger grazing animals, such as ducks and certain fishes and insects, which feed upon shoreline and submerged vegetation. Dependent upon the first-order consumers are the second- or third-order consumers, carnivorous animal plankton, fishes, insects, birds, and shore-dwelling mammals.

Another basic type of organism, not so well known but equally important, is the *decomposer*. Decomposers are microscopic organisms, bacteria and fungi. They are found in abundance along the bottom of the pond, strewn in a thin layer where the mud and water meet. They are also found in great numbers where plant plankton abounds, and along the shore among emergent plants. Less than half a teaspoonful of sediment from the bottom of a pond may contain over a million living bacteria. These bacteria and fungi are beneficial, although at times the results of their activity may be both unsightly and foul-smelling. Their value lies in their ability to break down organic substances and release their components into the water and air, where later they may be used by plants to start the whole production process over again. In the favorable temperatures of ponds, at least in summer, decomposition is rapid and nutrients are quickly released from dead plants and animals.

Assisting the microscopic decomposers are many *scavengers*, including animals that consume large quantities of *detritus*. This material, the fine, partly decomposed remains of plants and animals, coats the bottom and hangs suspended in the water.

A multitude of plants

When you visit a pond, you will be impressed by the luxuriant vegetation growing in and around it. To be sure, it accounts for a great deal of the primary production of the pond, but the microscopic plant plankton, or *phytoplankton*, is a more valuable food source for most animals. Ducks, some turtles, muskrats, certain fishes, and a few snails and insects depend upon the larger pond plants. The phytoplankton, however, nourishes almost every animal in the pond, directly or indirectly. In the warmer months of the year, phytoplankton is likely to be more abundant. If you sweep a fine conical plankton townet through the water, you might find that as much as ninety-three percent of all the organisms collected will be phytoplankton; only about seven percent will be small animals, or *zooplankton*. But this is not all. No matter how fine the net, many still tinier organisms, mostly plants, will escape through its meshes; indeed these may be ten times as numerous as all the netted plankton.

Although tiny animals will sometimes comprise only a small percentage of the plankton in your net, zooplankton is actually tremendously abundant. Look through a microscope at a drop of pond water from your net, and you will see hundreds upon hundreds of moving creatures. Most of these feed upon phytoplankton; they are miniature grazers in a watery pasture of great richness. You will find very few *predators*, or second-order consumers, among the freshwater plankton. There are only two that you are likely to see clearly without a microscope, the water flea *Leptodora* and the insect larva *Chaoborus*.

A fine-meshed townet such as this, drawn slowly through the open water of the pond, will collect a sample of plankton—small, mostly microscopic organisms that play a key role in the productivity of the pond. Plants make up the bulk of the plankton, and are of major importance in utilizing the enormous amount of solar energy reaching the pond. On a sunny day this energy is the equivalent of 4500 horsepower for every acre of the pond's surface!

Most second-order consumers are not planktonic but are considerably larger animals—small fish and insects that can swim where they will. They strain out quantities of zooplankton, and phytoplankton too, and in turn are eaten by still larger predators—insects, crustaceans, fish, frogs, turtles, and birds. The chain of consumers is not always a clear or direct one. Very few pond organisms eat only one special kind of food. Most graze on or capture whatever they can. If you study the food habits of certain consumers, however, you will quickly discover that they tend to eat what they can capture easily, what is abundant. At certain times of the year, some fish will gorge themselves exclusively upon midge larvae or mayfly nymphs.

The transfer of food energy from the pond's producers to successively higher orders of its consumers results in about a ninety percent loss at each step. Thus, a thousand pounds of plant plankton can produce only a hundred pounds of copepods; these in turn can be converted to ten pounds of mudminnows, which can add one pound to the weight of a snapping turtle. This pyramid effect accounts for the fact that a pond can support only a few large predators, such as snapping turtles and ospreys.

The transfer of energy

When an animal eats a plant or another animal, it gets the substances necessary for growth and repair as well as the energy these processes require. Consider the total amount of

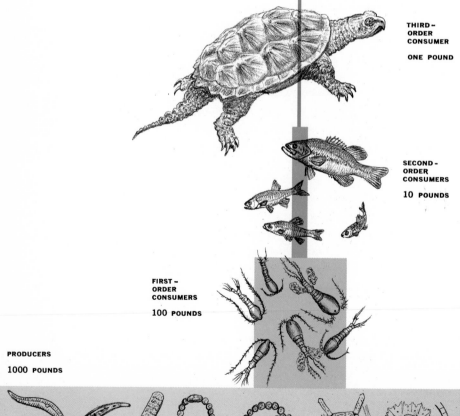

THIRD-ORDER CONSUMER

ONE POUND

SECOND-ORDER CONSUMERS

10 POUNDS

FIRST-ORDER CONSUMERS

100 POUNDS

PRODUCERS

1000 POUNDS

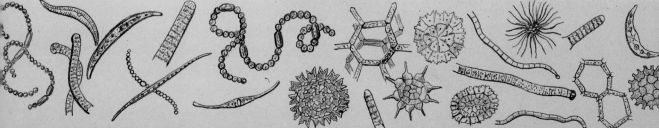

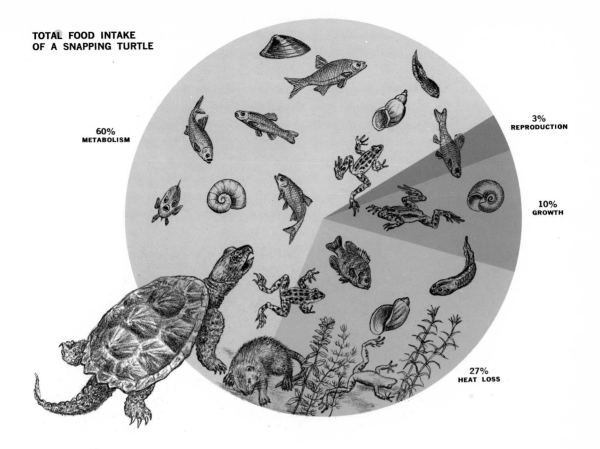

60%
METABOLISM

3%
REPRODUCTION

10%
GROWTH

27%
HEAT LOSS

plant food eaten by a copepod, a tiny shrimplike planktonic creature, as one hundred percent. Approximately sixty percent is used for the copepod's bodily activities—movement, breathing, heartbeat, digestion, and so on—known collectively as *metabolism*; ten percent is used for growth; and about three percent is used to develop eggs and sperm cells for reproduction. The remainder is lost, mostly dissipated in heat.

The transfer of energy-containing matter from one organism to another is very inefficient indeed. If you measure the total bulk of a number of organisms, the ten percent of energy used for growth becomes an important figure. Suppose a pond's population of copepods were nourished on ten thousand pounds of phytoplankton. The copepods' total weight would be only one-tenth of that figure, or one thousand pounds. Then, if these copepods were eaten, the second-order consumers would gain a total of only one hundred pounds. If these in turn were devoured, the third-order consumers would gain only ten pounds. A fourth-order con-

The reason for the successively narrower steps of the food pyramid shown on the opposite page becomes clear when you consider the disposition of the food energy consumed by an animal, such as the snapping turtle shown here. Of the turtle's total intake, roughly sixty percent is used up in metabolic processes of breathing, movement, digestion, and other bodily activities; three percent is allocated to reproductive products (sperm cells or eggs); twenty-seven percent is lost through heat dissipation and incomplete digestion. Thus, only ten percent remains to add to the actual growth of the turtle.

A pond is a temporary habitat: in time, the gradual accumulation of sediment and the forward advance of vegetation will transform the pond into a meadow. Lakes are subject to the same fate, but, owing to their larger size, the process takes longer and is less evident to a human observer. In the case of a pond, marked changes may take place in the span of a human lifetime.

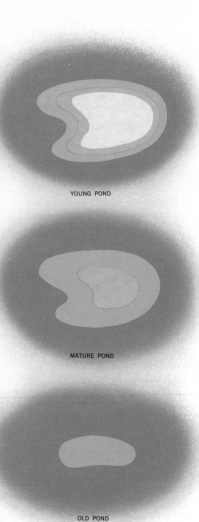

YOUNG POND

MATURE POND

OLD POND

sumer would gain one pound; and a fifth-order consumer, one-tenth of a pound. In other words, nine-tenths of the food a consumer eats is used up in its metabolic requirements or is lost; the food energy is given off primarily as heat and is not available again to any living organism. No wonder, then, that the activity of green plants is of such fundamental importance to animal life, whether in a pond or anywhere else on earth.

The relationships of the various producers and consumers in a community is sometimes described as a *pyramid of numbers*, because there are many more producer organisms than primary consumers, more primary consumers than second-order consumers, and so on. In the pond world, the number of diatoms staggers the imagination; the number of fish farther up the scale is large, but countable; the number of fourth-order consumers, however, is small, and a pond may support only half a dozen snapping turtles and a pair of ospreys.

Pond succession

A human lifetime is not long in the history of the earth, and during our lives we generally do not think much about changes in nature. The disappearance of a mountain range, of an island, or of a river takes too long for us to witness, but there is one gradual change we can watch during a lifetime: the birth, development, and eventual death of a pond.

The most obvious changes that you will notice around a pond take place as one form of plant follows, or succeeds, another. This process, called *succession,* occurs in nearly all the world's habitats, but nowhere is it more evident than in a pond.

The idea of succession is easy to grasp. It means simply that when a pond is first established, certain pioneer plants colonize its shores and, later, its bottom. Through the death and decay of these plants, the soil around and underneath the pond is enriched with organic nutrients that allow other, more demanding, plants to appear. These plants, in turn, die and decay; sediment builds up, and still different kinds of plants take root. As sediment accumulates, a pond becomes shallower and the shores reach in toward the center. The result, of course, is that the pond becomes smaller, until finally its opposing shores meet and there is no longer any

28

open water. The pond has ceased to exist; it is now only a wet spot in a meadow, and soon that, too, fills in and dries.

There is no one way in which pond succession takes place. The sequence of events varies according to latitude and altitude and according to many geological factors, such as the type of soil, the source of water, and so on. Purely biological factors influence succession, too. A pond may be affected by decaying plant matter in the water of a stream that feeds it or by organic pollution of some kind. Much depends on the nature of the first pioneers that establish themselves in the pond; they set the stage for most future developments. These factors, and many more, give character to a pond and make it different from all others.

In the beginning

Imagine that you can observe a man-made pond, located in one of the Middle Atlantic states, from its birth to its death. First you watch as a great hole is bulldozed in a field. Slowly the basin is filled by a small meandering stream that has run

Here is a very young pond, created by a bulldozer and, at the time this picture was made, only about six months old. The shore and bottom are still quite raw, but along the shoreline in the foreground are the beginnings of littoral vegetation, and in the shallows filamentous algae are starting to thrive. The green water indicates that plant plankton is flourishing. Although not visible in the photograph, a multitude of aquatic insects have sought out this new habitat and settled down in it.

TUNDRA PONDS AND PRAIRIE POTHOLES

Just as a variety of factors may produce a pond, so a variety of factors may determine its rate of succession, the series of changes that ultimately result in its transformation into dry land. The arctic tundra (*below left*), the vast barren plain extending from the tree line in Canada northward to the Arctic Ocean, is dotted with ponds by the million. Yet despite this superabundance of standing water, the region is a desert, receiving only about eight inches of rainfall per year. The bulk of the water shown here comes from melting ground ice; it persists because the cold climate allows little evaporation. Succession is very slow indeed. The cold and the short growing season discourage the growth of aquatic vegetation. Because rain is sparse, the ponds receive little silt wash-in from the surrounding land. The permanently frozen soil just inches below ground level keeps nutrients locked up. Since many of these ponds freeze all the way to the bottom during the long northern winter, only a few species of animal life can survive in them. Thus, the

ponds of the tundra persist for very long periods of time with little
visible change.

Compare this terrain with the pothole country of South Dakota
(*below right*). A few thousand years ago, when the last great
continental ice sheet retreated northward, this land looked much
like the tundra, but a warmer climate and a more generous annual
rainfall—plus man's agricultural activities—have greatly accelerated
the rate at which its ponds are transformed into meadow. In this
one view, in fact, you can see ponds in every stage of succession.
The one in the center of the picture shows virtually no littoral
vegetation. The faint outlines of some ponds can just barely be
discerned in the plowed fields, and are probably totally invisible
from the ground. Others, no doubt, have vanished entirely. Yet
even the Dakota plains are relatively cool and arid, and if we
traveled farther south into warmer and wetter regions, we would
find areas where ponds such as these would disappear in a generation
or two instead of in centuries.

through the field for a long time. The earth bottom of the pond is raw, without much in the way of organic matter and without any trace of aquatic vegetation. At first there are no animals either. But as the stream fills the depression, it brings with it seeds, spores, eggs, plant and animal plankton, and even some larger animals and floating plants. Other organisms arrive in the pond in surprising ways. The feet of wading and swimming birds act as a sort of ferry service for spores of algae, seeds, protozoan cysts, rotifer and crustacean eggs, worms, and even the eggs of the stickleback, a fish. Wind-borne seeds, perhaps of spike rushes and cattails, germinate along the damp shoreline, insects fly in, and soon life is evident where only weeks before there was none.

The earliest plankton in the new pond is already present, carried there by the stream—protozoans, rotifers, and single-celled algae. Before long, masses of filamentous algae grow abundantly, often rising to the surface, buoyed by oxygen bubbles. Beneath the surface appear miniature forests of simple branched plants with delicate stems.

One of these might be bladderwort, a tiny carnivorous plant that traps animals, which supplement the meager nutrients available to it. Already there are some fish brought in by the stream, perhaps a few members of the sunfish family that require clean, unsilted bottoms upon which to lay their eggs.

As the days pass, the stream continues to bring in silt and organic remains, which settle to the bottom. Even more important is the gentle microscopic rain of dead plankton that drifts downward. The larger plants also die from time

A new pond, even one scooped out of raw subsoil, begins to take on a plant and animal population as soon as it fills. Wading and swimming birds bring in a variety of passengers on their legs, including the eggs of fish, snails, and crustaceans. Flying aquatic insects migrate from nearby bodies of water, and on wet nights frogs may make the same journey overland. Wind-borne seeds germinate along the shore and establish a band of littoral vegetation.

to time and are decomposed by the decay bacteria that are everywhere in the water.

Nutrients from the soil begin to leach out, or dissolve, into the water. Soon seeds of other shoreline plants, such as rushes and sedges, germinate in soil from which they can extract nourishment.

The young pond

Before many months have passed, the new pond will be fringed with green vegetation, some of which extends into the water itself. Sunfish nest and feed in the shallows, insects skim the surface and dive to the bottom, and at night the guttural calls of grass frogs can be heard. The pond is alive and rapidly passing through its early youth. The transition to a more mature community has come gradually and almost without your being aware of it.

During a pond's early stages, pioneer plants produce far more organic matter than they consume, and this accumulation alters a pond habitat not only by providing more nutrients for the plants that come later but also by affecting the physical nature of the pond itself. Sediment building up along the shores and on the bottom fills in spaces between soil particles and encourages bacterial activity, perhaps with the result that there is less oxygen available for animals. Silt suffocates certain types of animals, or their eggs. Gradually the community changes as the organisms of the pond alter their own environment.

A pond in its prime

You must wait several years after your pond is formed to see its full range of inhabitants. During the long years of its maturity it will harbor more species than it ever did when it was young, or than it can when it sinks into old age.

As you approach the pond, you can see several distinct zones of vegetation, running more or less parallel to its shoreline. You pass through a thicket of young trees and shrubs—alders, willow, and buttonbush—that encircles the pond. Here also grow marsh marigold, grasses where waterfowl nest, horsetails, spearwort, golden club, pennywort, water mint, sedges, and rushes. The soil is marshy and spongy with saturated organic matter. Little standing water is visible, but as you step across the damp marsh soil, water squishes beneath your feet.

As the pond passes from youth into its prime, the makeup of its plant and animal population changes. Perhaps the most immediately noticeable change is the establishment of lush and clearly defined zones of vegetation. The marshy and overgrown shore attracts muskrats, chimney crayfish, and a variety of bird life. Larger predators such as pickerel and water snakes take up residence. An accumulation of sediment supports a community of burrowers and bottom feeders. In terms of different kinds of life, the pond is now at its peak.

The littoral zone

The next region is wetter and very swampy. Shallow water from the pond extends around the roots and stems of a variety of shoreline plants. This is the beginning of the littoral zone. Common plants here are blue flag, bur reed, spike rush, water dock, reed grass, cattails, bulrushes, and more sedges. They still are largely land plants, and only small portions of their stems are beneath the water. Chimney crayfish, muskrats, frogs, and water snakes live in this zone. Here you may see a heron standing amid the tall reeds,

waiting for a frog to reveal its presence by moving.

The next area is still part of the littoral zone, but you will find it almost impossible to explore it without getting wet. The plants are *emergents*, plants that, while rooted in the bottom, often pass through a foot or more of water. If tussock sedges grow here, you can step from one tussock to the next, using the dense grassy clusters as not-so-firm stepping stones. But if the plants are spike rushes, swamp loosestrife, or rafts of sphagnum moss or cattails, you will have very little to step on. Often there is a false bottom, composed of silt and light plant fragments; it looks solid enough until you step on it and then find yourself sinking a foot or more to the true bottom. Probably the best way of approaching this zone is by water, in a boat of shallow draft.

Plants of this zone are among the most active invaders of the pond world. By one means or another they march out into or across the water, gradually narrowing the diameter of the pond. Swamp loosestrife, also called water willow, sends out tough stems that arch over the pond and, when they enter the water, produce dozens of reddish roots that penetrate the bottom several feet from the parent plant. In one growing season water willow can "walk" a yard or more, and over a period of years a shoreline growth of this plant can conquer a large water area. Tussock sedges, as well as water willow, trap great quantities of sediment around their stems. When this sediment builds up into a layer of saturated soil, the area becomes a marsh zone, and is occupied by other plants better suited to the new conditions.

Sphagnum and some other plants narrow the shoreline in

INVADER FROM THE SHORE

Pictured above is Silver Spring Lake, a pond near the town of
Wellfleet on Cape Cod. The transformation of Silver Spring Lake
into a marshy meadow is being materially hastened by an encircling
growth of water willow, also known as swamp loosestrife. Water
willow is among the most aggressive of the invader plants that grow
in the pond's littoral zone. Classed as an emergent shrub, it sends up
corky two- to eight-foot-long stems that droop out over the pond
(*above right*) and send down roots (*right*) wherever they touch
water or mud. New plants arise from these roots; sediment and
debris trapped by dense tangles of water willow quickly build up
a substrate substantial enough to support other littoral vegetation,
robbing the pond of a yard or more of open water each growing
season.

36

In the security of the tall grass bordering the pond, this female mallard is incubating a clutch of eggs; within about a month, six to twelve downy yellow ducklings will hatch and will soon be bobbing along behind their mother on the pond's surface. The mallard drake, well known for his iridescent green head, takes no part in caring for the eggs or the young. Mallards are the most abundant of all our wild ducks.

quite another way. Sphagnum moss and various heath plants, with which sphagnum is often found, form floating rafts out over the margin of the pond. Toward their edges these rafts are easily submerged, and their tangled masses of roots, stems, and dead plants become packed with sediment that accumulates under them until they are solid and firm. Eventually these organic plant remains are compressed as new debris falls on top of them, and they turn into peat.

Away from the shore

A little farther out, the population of emergent plants is different. Their leaves are seldom held far above the water, unlike those of reed grass and cattails. Arrowheads, spike rushes, three-square rushes, pickerelweed, and purple loosestrife are a few of the many plants you will see here.

In the tangled forest of emergent plants, both above and beneath the water surface, animals of all sorts are active. Frogs live here, feeding mallards push their way between the plants, and long-billed marsh wrens and swamp sparrows bob up and down as they cling to the flexible stems. Red-winged blackbirds flutter in and out of the vegetation, the males in spring and early summer displaying their brilliant red wing patches with every motion. Painted and red-bellied terrapins feed on plants, and small snappers may invade the region to capture whatever they can.

This is the region where pond fish feed and spawn. Mud-minnows, black bullheads, and pickerel usually abound here. Spiders stretch their webs from stalk to stalk above the surface to capture the multitudes of flying insects that emerge from aquatic immature stages. Fisher spiders cling to stems and even enter the water to capture a swimming insect or a young fish. Snails, flatworms, creeping bottom-dwelling crustaceans (aquatic isopods and amphipods), and a variety of both immature and adult insects—the creeping water bugs, for example—are found in the shallow, sun-warmed water. On the surface film amid the forest of plant stems, whirligig beetles and water striders dart about.

Two plants common to the shallows of the pond margin are four-foot-high pickerelweed (*left*), named for the fish that often lurk among its submerged stems, and sphagnum (*right*), a low-growing moss that, given time, can transform the pond into a peat bog.

41

FISHES OF THE POND

Fishes found in ponds usually are more tolerant of wide seasonal temperature changes than those dwelling in lakes and other large bodies of water. They are also less demanding in their oxygen requirements than the fishes that live in fast-flowing rivers and streams. But apart from these common characteristics, the pond fishes display a diversity of adaptations to the wide variety of life zones and food organisms afforded by the pond. Some lurk near the bottom; others inhabit the brightly lit surface waters; still others seek the shelter of plant-tangled shallows. As fry these fishes may serve as food for insect larvae and other invertebrates, and as adults they may in turn feed upon these same creatures. A sampling of some of the more common species is shown on these two pages.

The largemouth bass (above), *which may reach three feet in length and weigh twenty pounds, is one of the pond's larger carnivores: crayfish, large insects, and other fish are among its favored food items. The foot-long yellow perch* (upper left) *is easy to recognize by its row of dark vertical stripes. In the early spring, it lays its eggs in a narrow ribbon several feet long, in the vegetation near the shore. The satinfin shiner* (lower left) *is typical of the small schooling fish of the pond. Its diet is largely vegetarian.*

The bullhead, shown at the right with its young, is a resident of the pond's bottom mud, where its whiskerlike sensory barbels help it locate anything edible, animal or vegetable. The female lays her eggs, which number about two thousand, in a nest built and guarded by the male. He protects the fry until they are large enough to fend for themselves.

Plants that float

There are not always clear-cut distinctions between emergent plants and plants that are buoyed up by the water. Spatterdock, for example, is a yellow pond lily whose leaves float on the water surface early in the spring. Later, as the leaf stems elongate and the water level falls, the enlarged leaves rise above the water. Spatterdock grows in such profusion that it crowds out all other plants and shades the water beneath its broad umbrellalike leaves.

Most other water lilies resemble the white water lily. Its long, slender stems curve gracefully beneath the water and never rise above it. White water lilies do not crowd out other floating plants and may grow alongside water crowfoot, pondweed, water shield, and floating heart.

In this profusion of floating leaves there also may be some of the world's smallest flowering plants, duckweed and watermeal, as well as the larger water fernworts and floating liverworts. They are not rooted to the bottom, but simply float at the surface in quiet coves.

All plants with leaves exposed to air have pores, or *stomates*, in the leaf blades which allow gases and water vapor to pass in and out. Plants that live on land usually have stomates on the undersurfaces of their leaves; but plants with leaves that rest flat on the water have stomates on the upper surface of their leaves.

If you examine a floating leaf carefully, you find an interesting adaptation to water. The upper surface of the leaf repels water; if water is sprinkled on it, the drops assume a spherical shape and run off easily. The underside does not have the same kind of surface. It is always wet and strongly attracted to the water. On a windy day the advantage of such an arrangement is obvious: if a gust of wind lifts and turns over a floating leaf, the upper surface repels the water and the next gust quickly turns the leaf back to its proper position. As soon as the underside touches the water surface, it is immediately held down. It takes quite a bit of force to

Even the one-eighth-inch leaves of duckweed (*left*) seem large alongside those of watermeal, its close relative. These tiny floating plants share the pond's surface with the much larger pads of the white water lily (*upper right*) and with those of the yellow water lily, or spatterdock (*lower right*), which becomes more emergent in its habit as the growing season progresses.

44

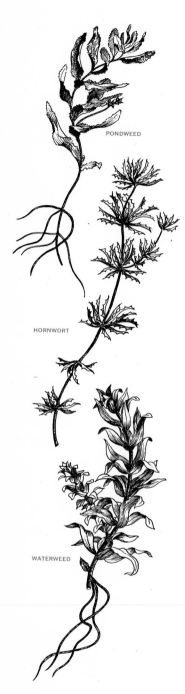

PONDWEED

HORNWORT

WATERWEED

overturn or submerge one of these leaves.

Mallards and pied-billed grebes swim and feed among the floating plants. Beneath them, pickerel lurk quietly; sunfish, perch, speckled bullheads, and chubsuckers swim about feeding, and perhaps being fed upon by larger consumers.

Wave action is reduced by the floating leaves and their slender stems, but not eliminated. When a wind blows, the leaves rise and fall gently with the small waves. Occasionally they are jerked suddenly as a turtle thrusts its way among the stems. Beyond the floating plants there is nothing but open water. Out there, in the limnetic zone, are the plankton feeders, such as shiners, and larger predacious fish. Mergansers swim low in the water, diving frequently beneath the surface to capture fish, frogs, and fresh-water mussels.

Plants beneath the surface

Out where the wind raises wavelets on a pond surface, there still is plant growth, but most of it is well below the surface. The plants that grow there seldom reach the air, except to produce flowers. Some submerged plants are seed producers and are quite complex; others are very primitive forms that reproduce by means other than seeds. Some of the pondweeds, particularly the crimped-leaf pondweed, grow in great beds and apparently choke out other bottom-dwelling plants. Where these weeds do not dominate, other submergents will appear: water celery, water milfoil, waterweed, fanwort, hornwort, and bladderwort, to mention only a few. How extensive the zone of submerged plants in a pond is depends almost entirely on how transparent the water is. If plankton is densely concentrated, or if the water is constantly opaque with suspended silt particles, then light cannot filter far down, and the zone where photosynthesis can take place is necessarily a shallow one. In some ponds, however, the water is clear, and green plants can be found growing fifteen or twenty feet below the surface.

Long strands of water milfoil reach upward from the pond's bottom toward the life-sustaining sunlight at the surface. Milfoil, whose name means "thousand leaves," is among the most common of *submergents*—plants that grow completely underwater, except for aerial flower stalks.

46

RICH WATERS
AND POOR

For a variety of reasons, physical and chemical, ponds contain differing quantities of the materials necessary for life, such as oxygen, carbon dioxide, and various compounds of nitrogen, calcium, potassium, and phosphorus. Ponds that are rich in these materials are designated as *eutrophic* ("richly nourishing") by biologists, and those that are poor in them are designated as *oligotrophic* ("scantily nourishing"). The pond shown at the left is eutrophic: note the crowded zones of littoral vegetation and, in the underwater view, the relative murkiness of the water, indicating a teeming plankton community. The pond on the right, on the other hand, is oligotrophic: its shore is virtually free of emergent vegetation, and its water is so devoid of plankton that sunlight penetrates all the way to the bottom, where only a few submergent plants struggle to live in the wet wasteland. In general, warm, shallow, southern ponds tend to be eutrophic; cold, deep, northern ponds are likely to be oligotrophic.

Animals feed among the submerged plants, but not so intensively as they do in the shoreward zones. Aquatic insects are not so abundant here as they are closer to shore. The few that are present usually sprawl on the bottom or swim close to the mud from one sheltering clump of vegetation to the next. Crayfish are common and share the region with a variety of fishes.

The zonation of animals

While plant zonation is easy to see in the pond, it is also true that, to a lesser extent, there is a pattern to the animal life as well. Different species of water birds frequent distinct zones: mallards and black ducks habitually feed close to shore; geese and swans feed a little farther out, possibly because their longer necks enable them to reach deeper bottoms; and diving ducks and grebes feed in still deeper regions. Pond fish also tend to be partial to certain zones in the pond, depending upon the species. And the pond's

A pond passes from its prime into the beginnings of old age with surprising rapidity. The picture below shows Mud Pond, near the town of Morgan in northern Vermont, as it appeared in 1960. The picture on the opposite page was taken from the same spot, in the same season of the year, in 1966. In just six years, advancing bulrushes and cattails have carried the shoreline far out into what had been the realm of open water.

insect population may be zoned as well. There is evidence, for example, that some species of water boatmen, or corixids, live among the densely vegetated zone of emergent plants, while other species live farther out in open water.

Other evidence of animal zonation may be found in the sediments of the bottom. Using fine sieves, biologists have discovered variations in the sizes of particles from the shore of a pond to its center, and also in the amount of fine organic matter as distinguished from silt of nonliving origin. Depending on the size of the particles, burrowing animals may or may not be present, and so apparently even these creatures are zoned.

The aging pond

The mature pond, with its rich variety of life, is now beginning to slip into old age. One day you realize that there is much less water than there was in the past and that certain types of plants and animals are not so plentiful as they once

were. The bottom is even thicker with muck. Floating plants have bridged across the pond, and no longer are there any submerged forms. Young forest trees grow from what long ago was pond shore. Open-water fishes are gone, and many of the turtles seem to have migrated elsewhere.

Now imagine that the passage of time has accelerated, and you see the pond in its old age. Much of what was once pond is now marsh. Only small regions of open water remain, and these evaporate during the drier seasons of the year. Invading emergent plants have captured the entire pond basin, with shrubs and trees following close behind. The floating plants have vanished, and there is little animal life in the remaining water.

In the shallow temporary parts of the pond, where fish cannot live, there is a new kind of succession that is related to seasonal drying up. During March, large salamanders breed in the shallow pools. By late March and April, *Cyclops*, a common copepod crustacean, abounds and usually is followed by fairy shrimp and another species or two of copepod. In May small flatworms might be breeding in the remaining puddles, but all standing water is gone by June. The rest of the summer the region is inhabited by terrestrial insects, earthworms, and other creatures of the land.

What has happened to this old pond? Decomposed aquatic plants, leaves, logs and sticks brought in by beavers and muskrats, and silt carried by water flowing from the land have all helped to fill it in. And as it filled, the shoreline

As the pond passes from its prime into old age, its plant and animal population declines both in variety and in abundance. Floating and emergent plants now cover the entire surface, choking out the submergents below. Invading littoral vegetation carries the shoreline farther out each year, and a layer of deep sediment now clogs the bottom. The pond is gradually being transformed into a marsh.

advanced. With so much decay going on, oxygen is not so plentiful in the water as it was, and there are very few submerged plants or planktonic plants to replenish it. Many animals can no longer breed and raise their young under these conditions. The only fishes left in the few deeper puddles are golden shiners, bullheads, and mudminnows, and even the shiners may be dying out. Sedges, rushes, or cattails cover the whole pond area and now provide good breeding places for some smaller frogs—spring peepers, cricket frogs, and the like—that have difficulty surviving in larger ponds where there are many active predators.

Although certain types of plants have disappeared from the old pond forever, others flourish and the region remains densely populated. Plant and animal plankton still exist, and may persist as long as any water is present. But the water continues to diminish, and the entire habitat finally becomes a temporary pond that disappears in the summer. All the fish vanish, of course, although frogs, salamanders, burrowing crayfish, leeches, and snails remain. Snails resist drying by secreting a film of mucus that seals the shell opening; leeches produce mucus-lined cocoons around themselves; and the other animals either burrow into damp soil or find security and moisture under dense vegetation. In the rich soil there are countless cysts and spores of algae, bacteria, yeasts, fungi, protozoans, rotifers, and other small organisms. When rains create puddles, these spores and cysts open and the tiny organisms that emerge lead active, if brief, lives.

The death of a pond

And so, your pond is gone. In its place is a lush green meadow that has its own patterns of succession. The meadow will continue to change for many years to come, going from a grassland to a thicket of shrubs, on to various communities of trees, and finally to a forest.

A pond seen today is only an event in time, a moment in a sequence that reaches into the past and extends into the future. A pond, like a lake, has its birth, its youth, its maturity, its old age, and finally its death. A lake can exist for thousands of years, if it is large and deep, but a small pond may appear and disappear in less than a century. What today is but a wet depression in a meadow might very well have been a sizable pond in your grandfather's time.

As mortal as a living thing, this pond, in the span of a
century or two, has experienced birth, youth, maturity,
old age, and death. Eventually this site will be
overgrown by a young forest.

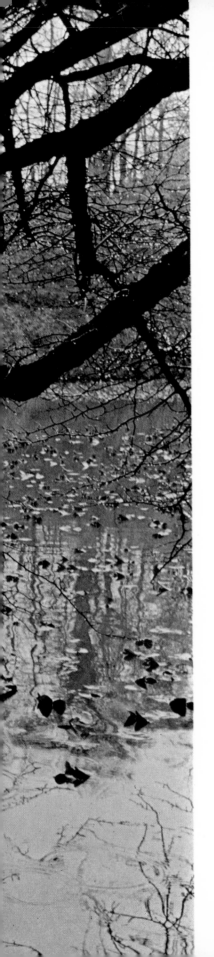

Seasons and Days

Ponds in the United States are greatly affected by the seasons, with their varying temperatures, light, and rainfall. Because they are shallow and exposed, ponds quickly warm up in the spring and cool off in the fall, and there is a constantly changing parade of life as the seasons go by. A pond may dry up altogether in summer, or it may freeze to the bottom in winter, and these events determine what kinds of animals and plants can live in it. During the weeks of any one season, there are also variations that can affect the life of a pond. A few days of unusually warm weather in late winter may cause aquatic plants to bloom far ahead of time. Or severe floods in the spring may prevent some shoreline plants from flowering properly. And there are daily variations in temperature and light, which have an easily observable effect upon the life of a pond, just as they do upon the plants and animals of the land and sea.

The geographical location of a pond also influences what goes on within it. Plants in the North begin to grow later in the calendar year than do those in the South. During the long northern winter nutrients accumulate in a pond, and when summer comes there is explosive growth and multiplication of plankton, a phenomenon that biologists call a plankton bloom.

Let us look at one typical pond in the temperate middle latitudes of this country and see what happens in a year's time.

The coming of spring

As winter draws to a close and the sun climbs a little higher each day, the ice covering the pond vanishes and life stirs. The increasing length of the days triggers the renewed activity of many organisms, for the water is still very cold and warms only slowly at first. The pond is ripe for life: its water is high, full of dissolved oxygen, and slightly alkaline.

In the marshy soil along the banks of the pond, skunk

Among the earliest signs of spring is the emergence of the mottled flower hoods and bright green leaves of skunk cabbage, which often force their way up through the still frozen marshy margin of the pond. The foul odor that gives the plant its common name has been described as resembling skunk, garlic, rotting meat—and a combination of all three.

cabbages unfold their flowers and then their leaves from tight colorful buds that pushed up from the damp ground weeks earlier. Buds on many emergent plants open to reveal small green shoots that lengthen with every passing day. In quiet coves, masses of green algae rise to the water's surface, buoyed by oxygen bubbles given off as by-products of photosynthesis. A few duckweed and watermeal plants that survived the winter dot the surface.

During the first bright days of spring the winter plankton still remains, but within a week or so there are signs of the great plankton bloom that is to come: phytoplankton increases—diatoms, flagellates, and desmids. In shallow water along the shores, the eggs of rotifers and water fleas hatch, adding to the zooplankton. Water fleas and copepod crustaceans reproduce in great numbers.

Many of the insect larvae that passed the winter in a nearly dormant state now become hungry and active. Dragonfly and damselfly nymphs stalk across the bottom on the dead remains of last year's vegetation, seeking prey which they capture with hinged, expansible jaws that shoot out rapidly before the victim can escape. Amphipods and isopods that swam slowly about beneath the ice during the winter now go about their activities in a more frenzied manner. On a sunny day, among the dead and dried stalks of old emergent plants, you can find water striders skimming the surface. Water beetles make their appearance, but not yet in large numbers.

Western skunk cabbage differs from its eastern counterpart in possessing bright yellow flower hoods. The two plants are not close relatives, but they are similar in habit and habitat. The odor they emit, so offensive to the human nose, is nevertheless highly attractive to certain species of flies that move from plant to plant and carry out the vital task of pollination.

59

Hooded mergansers frequent
secluded woodland ponds,
where they nest in hollow trees,
in stumps, or underneath
overhanging banks. The
birds are easily identified by
the male's fan-shaped black and
white crest, which can be
raised or lowered and which
plays an important role in his
colorful courtship ritual. Less
vegetarian than many ducks,
mergansers include quantities of
fish, frogs, and other animal
foods in their diet. Because of
the resultant "gaminess" of their
flesh, the birds are molested by
human hunters to a lesser
degree than some of their more
herbivorous, and therefore more
tasty, relatives.

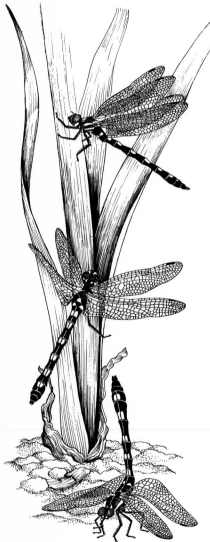

In its threat posture (*top*), a dragonfly flicks its wings open and elevates its abdomen about forty-five degrees from the surface on which it is resting. On warm days, a resting dragonfly may use its wings to shade its abdomen (*center*). On very hot days, the insect shields its thorax with its wings and points its abdomen upward (*bottom*) so that it receives as little direct sunlight as possible.

Soon the first waterfowl of the season arrive from the South. You can see common mergansers, ring-necked ducks, and pied-billed grebes diving deep into the pond's cold waters. And on a bright day you may also glimpse a muskrat swimming through the dry reeds that rattle in the chill wind.

Under the warming sun certain tiny flies known as midges emerge from their pupal cases at the surface, take wing, and mate hovering over the pond. These are the first of the pond's insects to fly in the clear spring air, but their adult lives are short and are often over before the cold night comes.

The bass and sunfish that spent the winter in deeper water now come close to shore to feed on the tiny organisms that appear with every new day. On warm days spring peepers call from marshy spots deep in a wooded cove. A few frogs appear in shallow water, but they are quiet.

As May approaches, the pond bursts with life. The warming sun has raised the temperature of the surface water several degrees. Two or three species of pond snails join the amphipods and isopods. Planarian flatworms begin depositing their stalked cocoons on pebbles and submerged sticks; after only a week or two, several tiny, almost colorless planarians crawl out of the ruptured cocoons and begin their life on the bottom of the pond.

The dragonflies

Dragonflies now make their appearance, having crawled as nymphs onto plant stems above the surface. By mid-May there are a great many of them darting above the pond. They capture emerging and flying insects by grasping them with their legs, which form a kind of basket.

You can learn a great deal about dragonflies simply by sitting quietly by a pond. Perhaps a dragonfly will rest for a while on a bare twig near you and watch for passing insects. You will then be able to see its extremely large eyes and mobile neck. Every so often, its head will twist about quickly as it sights some passing prey. Most of the dragon-

This dragonfly spent the first year of its life as a nymph, an active predator of the pond bottom. Now it has crawled up a plant stem, molted its final nymphal skin, and emerged as a winged adult, one of the most superbly skillful fliers of the insect world.

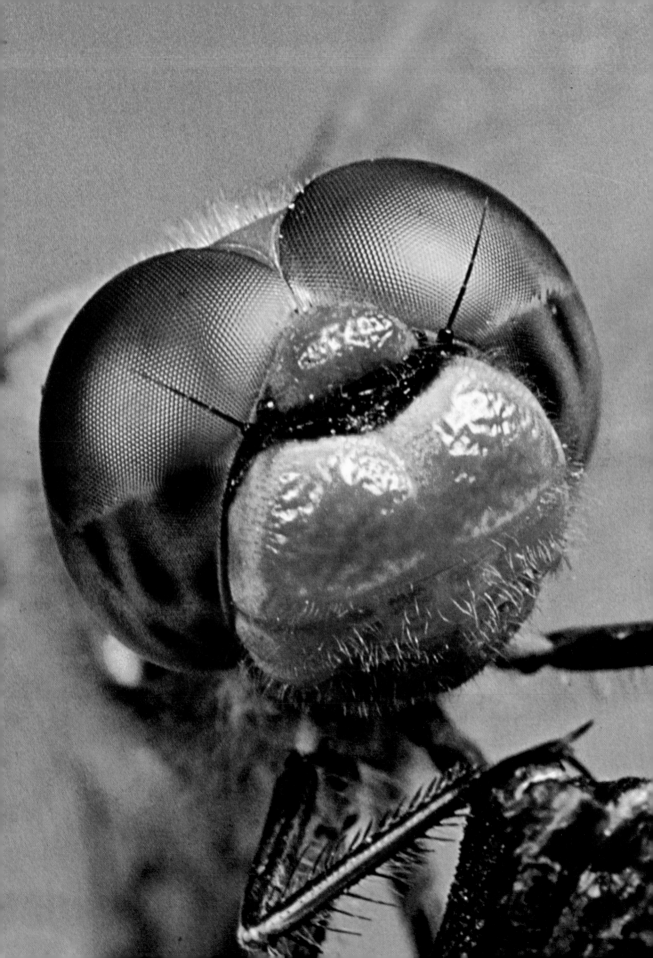

The dragonfly owes much of its skill in capturing small flying insects to the pair of huge compound eyes that cover most of its head. In some species, these remarkable organs each comprise thirty thousand individual facets, giving the dragonfly an exceptionally wide sphere of vision.

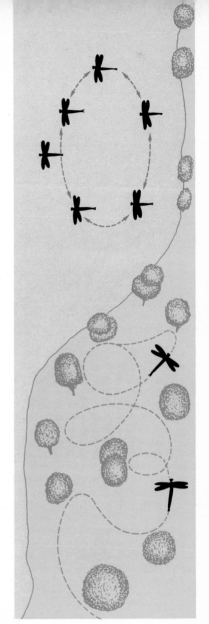

flies found around ponds do not spend much time perching, but fly back and forth along the shore, at times speeding out to the center of the pond. They can fly twenty miles an hour, fast enough to capture most other insects and to escape pursuing birds. A dragonfly is an extremely agile flier and can change direction, hover, and rise more effectively than any helicopter. It even has air brakes: it can slow down in midair by lowering its abdomen and hind legs and interrupting the flow of air.

The posture of a perched dragonfly changes with the temperature. If the day is warm, but not hot, the insect will rest flat on a twig with its wings adjusted to shade its abdomen. If the day is very hot, it may raise its abdomen almost vertically, away from the hot surface on which it is resting.

Occasionally a dragonfly will elevate its entire body about forty-five degrees from a surface in what appears to be a threatening gesture. This stance may have some special meaning for other insects, but you should consider it pure bluff, for dragonflies are harmless to man.

Dragonflies usually range up and down a pond shoreline, but for a while one may adopt a certain territory as its own and drive all others away. Feeding flights are rather circular, looping affairs. Flights that have reproductive significance are different: males patrol back and forth along the shore, hovering and facing open water at regular intervals. These patrol flights do not overlap one another, and mating territories as a result are quite distinct.

Creatures of the late spring

By late May, water beetles are numerous. In flight, they seem to be attracted by the reflection of the sun on water, and they descend to take up residence in pools and ponds far from the places where they emerged. It is not surprising that water beetles and some other flying aquatic insects, such as water boatmen and backswimmers, can thrive even

Dragonfly behavior is interesting and varied, and makes a good subject for pondside study. A male dragonfly, for example, may stake out a portion of the shore as a territory and patrol it by hovering at set positions along its length. In contrast, the same insect's feeding flight is a continuous, more or less random, search for flying insects over the countryside around the pond.

65

in temporary ponds. When the water dries up, they simply fly away.

Now is the time that alderflies and crane flies emerge and mayfly nymphs crawl to the surface. The fluttering mayfly adults rise from some ponds and lakes in enormous numbers and carpet nearby fields and streets with their bodies, especially where they are attracted by lights.

In late spring, the reproductive activity of frogs is at its height. You can hear the distinctive calls of these amphibians booming over the pond during early evening—the snore of the pickerel frog, the plucked banjo string of the green frog, and over it all, the sonorous roar of the great bullfrog.

As the water warms, decay bacteria become increasingly abundant. These vital decomposers break down organic matter on the bottom into simple compounds that plants can use. All spring the water has been growing steadily more opaque with phytoplankton, and now it is a yellow-green color. But the pond water is not "dirty," for it contains very few soil particles. Almost every mote that interrupts the passage of light through the water is a living plant or animal, and those that are not alive are organic particles, mostly bits of decaying plant tissue.

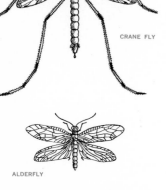

CRANE FLY

ALDERFLY

Early days of summer

By mid-June the water of the pond has a gradual but definite temperature gradient: it is warm on top and cool underneath. The pond is too small to be stirred much by currents or by winds, and so the warm water tends to stay at the surface. From the top to the bottom of the deepest water, a distance of about six feet, there is a temperature difference of nearly ten degrees, but there is no sharp boundary line as there would be in a lake. Many of the fishes prefer to stay in the deeper, cooler water during the day. The sunfish, however, continue to guard their nests in the shallows along the shore. Their eggs, which are glued to pebbles in cleared depressions, are incubated best in warm water. The male parent fish constantly fan the nests with their fins, washing away debris and silt that might settle upon the eggs and circulating the water so that the developing embryos are always surrounded by fresh, oxygenated water.

Populations of some animals continue to increase during early summer, but most level off and decrease as the pond

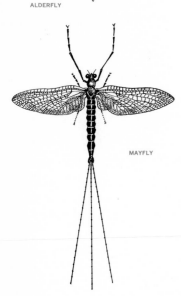

MAYFLY

66

becomes even warmer. In June, pond snails are abundant, and you can find their clear gelatinous egg masses on almost every leaf, twig, and stone in shallow water. The little mudminnow and grass pickerel lurk among the weeds, where recently hatched sunfish and bass congregate in schools. Some pond fish swim in schools when they are young and later become solitary in habit. For a young fish, there is safety in numbers; a mudminnow or pickerel has difficulty singling out one victim when it is confronted with so many flashing, fleeing shapes.

The tadpoles are growing rapidly, and some of those that hatched from eggs in the spring already are beginning to develop legs. First to appear are the hind legs, which trail functionless under the tail. Later the front legs emerge, one through the pore from the gill chamber and then the other through skin on the opposite side of the head. (True frogs and toads have only one opening to the gill chamber, on their left sides.) Also, the tadpoles' mouths are beginning to change from tiny rasping, sucking beaks to wide jaws, and their eyes are starting to bulge a bit. By midsummer, their legs are stronger, their tails are partially absorbed, their jaws are developing, their nostrils are fully formed, and they are breathing air and putting their heads above the water. Soon they leave the water altogether and spend their time hunting for insects in the grass along the marshy shores.

This male green frog, attempting to attract a mate, joins in the chorus of a late spring evening along the pond margin. The frog's mouth and nostrils are kept tightly closed when it calls. Air is driven back and forth between mouth and lungs, with the inflated throat sacs acting as resonating chambers.

67

FROM TADPOLE
TO FROG

Among all the vertebrate animals, from the most primitive fishes to man himself, no creatures undergo such radical changes while maturing as the members of the order Salientia, the frogs and their relatives the toads. In its body form, the larval frog, or tadpole, is totally fishlike; as an adult it is a four-legged land dweller. Like a fish, the tadpole breathes with gills; the adult breathes with lungs. The tadpole is herbivorous, feeding primarily on algae which it rasps off underwater surfaces with a round, jawless beak. The adult frog is an omnivorous feeder, equipped with a wide, jawed mouth and a long, sticky tongue that flicks out to capture insects and other

1

2

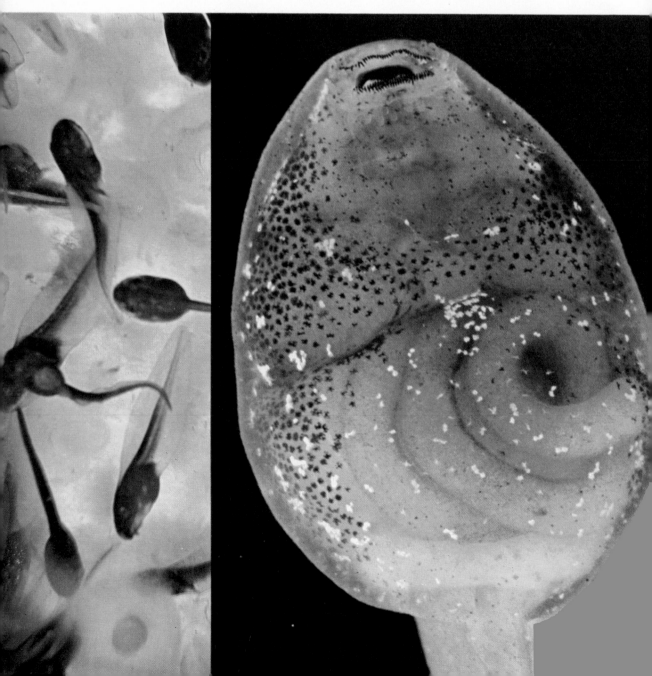

prey. Even the animal's heart undergoes major structural changes, transforming from the two-chambered organ typical of the fishes to the three-chambered one that represents the next step up on the evolutionary scale. Indeed, the metamorphosis of a tadpole into an adult frog or toad symbolizes many of the complex changes in body form which were required when backboned animals first left the water millions of years ago and took up life on the land. It is worth reflecting that, in a sense, this momentous event in the history of life is reenacted in miniature each time a newly transformed frog crawls out of the pond into the light and air.

3

Newly hatched frog tadpoles (1) are essentially fishlike creatures, and give little indication of the radically different form they will assume as adults. The tadpole's vegetarian diet is reflected by its unusually long intestine—a characteristic of plant eaters—visible through its translucent belly skin (2). A fully formed tadpole (3) is almost perfectly fishlike: note the fin-fringed tail with crisscross layers of muscle much like that of a fish. The eyes, like a fish's, are set on the side of the head, giving a wide field of view but not the partial binocular vision that the prey-catching adult will need. A tadpole even possesses the lateral line of a fish, a special sensory system for detecting vibrations and pressure changes in the water. This will disappear in the adult. Metamorphosis of the tadpole into a frog is triggered by the thyroid gland. One of the first signs of approaching adulthood is the emergence of tiny, nonfunctional hind limbs (4). Once legs have appeared, changes are rapid and radical. . . .

4

5

6

. . . Metamorphosis from tadpole to frog is well under way
above (5). The hind legs, although not yet strong enough to
be truly functional, are growing rapidly. Nostrils are beginning
to appear, heralding the changeover from gills to lungs. In time,
the tadpole becomes definitely froglike (6): the jaws are
beginning to form; the eyes are assuming a more elevated
position on the head; eyelids are developing; the nostrils are
becoming more prominent; and all four limbs are present and
large enough to be at least somewhat functional. . . .

7

. . . *The creature is now half tadpole, half frog (7). Its limbs are fully functional, but it can still use its tail for swimming. Its gills may still be partially functional, but it now comes to the surface from time to time to fill its newly formed lungs with air. The full-fledged frog (8) has only a tail stump remaining as a reminder of its fishlike larval life. In a few weeks more this stump will be completely absorbed into the body.*

8

Birds of the pond

The summer birds have now flown in, and most of the water-fowl have gone on to the North. Only a few mallards, black ducks, and grebes remain; many of them nested in the high shoreline vegetation and led their newly hatched young into the pond. Ducklings follow close behind their mother, bound to her by an instinctive, invisible tether from the moment they have hatched. But they are not completely safe, for beneath the water are skillful predators—snapping turtles and large pickerel or bass that can snatch a duckling from the surface.

In a cove, among reed grass and spatterdock, stands a great blue heron, a huge, majestic bird that is wary and difficult to approach. With a quick thrust of its long neck and its spearlike bill, it captures a bluegill that has been basking in the shallows. After gulping down the fish, the great bird springs into the air, and with slow, measured beats of its broad wings flies on to another cove. There it settles into the water as before and stands, head erect, watching for another fish or a frog to move and reveal its presence.

Other herons live around the pond, too. A common egret or a green heron often perches on a dead tree limb hanging over the water. And several little blue herons are almost always present. When you paddle your boat into a cove, they take off with protesting croaks and fly to a less disturbed spot.

You may see a conspicuously marked gray-blue and white bird swoop down from a tree, skim the water, and with a loud, rattling cry dart up into a shoreline tree again. It is the kingfisher, one of the pond's best known birds. In some parts of the country it must be protected by law, for misinformed fishermen think that it captures too many game fish. Although it eats some young fish, its diet also includes

Perhaps the most spectacular of the pond's bird visitors is the great blue heron, which may reach a height of four feet or more. The long, sharp beak is a dual-purpose weapon: as the bird wades through the shallows, small game is snapped up and swallowed on the spot; large fish are impaled and carried to shore, where they are clubbed into senselessness and swallowed headfirst. In addition to fish, the great blue heron feeds on frogs, crustaceans, insects, snakes, and even small birds and mammals.

The crow-sized green heron is a patient fisherman, standing motionless on a limb over the water. If an unwary shiner or sunfish comes within striking range, the bird will dart forward and snap up its catch with lightning speed. At breeding time, the female green heron lays a clutch of three to nine eggs in a nest of sticks in a tree or shrub not far from the water. Both parents share in incubating the eggs and caring for the young.

HONKERS OF THE POND

Of the many water birds that use our northern ponds as summer nurseries, none is more widely known than the big, stately Canada goose. Ready to breed at the age of two or three years, goose and gander mate for life. A nest of sticks and grass is built—frequently atop a beaver lodge—and the female lays from five to nine buff-colored eggs, which she incubates for about a month. During this time, the gander vigilantly guards his nesting mate; a human venturing too near the nest site is almost certain to be driven away by a furious attack from the big male bird. Two days after hatching, the downy yellow goslings are led down to the water by both parents, who continue to care for their offspring throughout the summer. When the days shorten, the Canada geese leave their breeding ponds and head south again.

insects, frogs, mice, crayfish, and even berries. Certainly kingfishers do more good than harm. A decline in the population of pond fish can nearly always be traced to a decreasing food supply, and very seldom to large predators.

The pond at dusk

A pond in summer is a fascinating place. You can learn a lot by sitting down next to the water's edge and watching what goes on around you. Probably you will not have the time, or the patience, to spend twenty-four consecutive hours there, but it would be well worth your while to visit the pond at intervals during the day and night. The pace of life in and around the pond constantly changes as the hours pass.

At dusk, water lilies have already closed their petals, and many animals are quiet. Some creatures, however, are most active during the hours just preceding darkness. Yellow perch feed busily now, and midges dance over the water. Dozens of swallows skim the quiet water, catching some of the midges and other flying insects that have just transformed from aquatic nymphs and pupae. Every now and then a swallow will furrow the surface as it scoops up water to drink.

It is during daylight hours that most midges and mosquitoes emerge from their aquatic pupae to become adults, though a few seem to prefer early evening. The whole transformation takes only a matter of seconds. First you see a wriggling pupa rise to the surface from the muddy bottom. As soon as the pupa hits the surface film, it splits down the back. The adult midge pops out, stands on the empty pupa skin for a moment, and then takes wing. During the emergence, the pupal case often darts across the water. This action may be caused by a secreted substance and may help the adult to emerge and dry off its damp folded wings.

As darkness falls, silent winged creatures follow strange irregular courses over the pond; they are little brown bats pursuing moths, midges, and other flying insects, which they locate by means of their remarkable sonar system. A few of the moths are able to "tune in" on the bats' ultrasonic cries, and their evasive actions make the aerial chases even more erratic.

76

The pond at night

With darkness, the pace of life in the pond slackens. Phytoplankton and shoreline plants no longer manufacture food and release oxygen; instead they consume oxygen and use it to extract energy from stored food. A barred owl hoots along the shore, but most birds are sleeping. If you move slowly and quietly to the water's edge and shine a flashlight into shallow water, you may see fish resting almost motionless on the bottom. Only their gently waving fins betray their presence. Since fish have no eyelids to close, they may seem to be awake, but they are not.

Frogs are active in the early evening; then, as night wears on, they call less and finally fall silent.

Most aquatic insects and crustaceans seem to be as active at night as they are in the daytime. Indeed, because you can see them easily with a flashlight at night, they appear to be even more abundant and more active. Amphipods dash from under leaves and fallen limbs, swimming rapidly on their sides. Below them, the slower isopods crawl over decayed vegetation, scavenging bits of organic matter.

Try hanging over the edge of a dock or over the side of a boat at night, with your face close to the water surface. Shine your flashlight straight down and look for the individual members of the zooplankton twisting and turning through the water. If your eyes are good and you look closely, you will be able to distinguish various animals: copepods swimming with skips and stops, water fleas swimming jerkily, ostracods swimming rapidly close to the bottom, water mites swimming smoothly over the bottom, large rotifers swimming smoothly near the surface. If you are very attentive, you may even see one of the larger protozoans, *Paramecium*, swimming evenly in a spiral path.

Once you get used to looking at organisms of this size, you are startled when a relatively huge water beetle comes dashing along. Then you realize that from the point of view of a nearly microscopic planktonic creature, this insignificant pond is a vast world indeed. Being so large ourselves, we tend to be aware of only the largest creatures. If the sizes of typical adults of every one of the world's animal species were tabulated, the average probably would be about that of a house fly. And, of course, the average size of all pond-dwelling species would be very much smaller.

A new day

As dawn approaches, yellow perch start feeding actively
again. Water boatmen, aquatic beetles, leeches, and planarian flatworms move about more. Later, when the sun
shines directly on the pond, many of these creatures tend
to congregate under submerged logs and stones, and in the
shade of vegetation. (Because they move slowly in the dark
and rapidly in the light, they inevitably collect in dark, protected places.) Frogs and turtles become more active now
that they can use their eyes for hunting.

Aquatic animals react to the sun's warmth in various
ways. Many of the larger ones seek the shade of floating
leaves or submerged objects. Turtles and snakes emerge
from the water and bask in the sun.

As the water becomes warmer, it holds less dissolved
oxygen, and some animals begin to have difficulty breathing. Tube-dwelling midge larvae and burrowing *Tubifex*
worms increase their waving and thrashing movements, thus
bringing more water their way. The lower the oxygen content of the water becomes, the farther they stick out of
their tubes and the faster they wave. Fish rise to the surface to breathe the oxygen diffusing into the water from the
air. Some insects must make frequent trips to the surface to
replenish bubbles of air that they carry underwater. Damselfly nymphs climb up the stems of emergent plants and
place their leaflike abdominal gills against the surface film.

By late afternoon the water temperature begins to fall,
breathing becomes easier, and the pace of life in the pond
becomes less frantic. As dusk approaches, many animals begin to feed more actively.

The threat of drying

Summer is not always a time of plenty for pond animals.
It can be a time of death or dormancy, when all the water
in a shallow pond evaporates to reveal a sun-baked brick-

The early morning mist drifting across the water marks
the start of a new day in the pond. Some creatures are
now stirring into activity, and others are retiring to
hideouts to await the return of darkness.

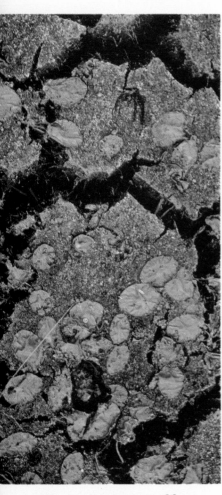

These yellowing water lily leaves embedded in cracked mud once floated on the surface of a shallow pond. The hot summer sun can reduce a flourishing pond to a bone-dry wasteland. In the face of such a catastrophe, some of the pond's residents migrate to other waters. Others, less mobile, either perish or go into a state of suspended animation to await the replenishing rains of autumn.

hard bottom. It seems improbable, but many of the pond's organisms survive drying and reappear after the autumn rains and winter snows. Bacteria and protozoans survive long droughts in microscopic spores and cysts. Snails, pill clams, water fleas, copepods, ostracods, leeches, and a variety of other purely aquatic animals enter a state of suspended animation, or *estivation*, as the mud hardens around them. Certain ostracods and water fleas have been known to estivate for twenty years, and fairy shrimp may estivate for even longer periods.

Most insects are not bothered particularly by a drying pond, although those that are entirely aquatic in their habits during their nymphal and larval stages may die if they cannot complete their development before all the water evaporates. A few kinds of mosquitoes actually have to complete their life cycles in temporary ponds. They usually deposit their eggs in dry depressions; after rain fills these puddles or little ponds, larvae emerge and begin their active lives.

Larger adult aquatic insects easily survive droughts, for most of them are capable of migrating elsewhere. Frogs and turtles, too, can seek more favorable habitats. Among the larger animals, only fish are unable to escape a drying pond.

The waning of summer

By July the larger organisms of the pond are fully developed and in their prime. Phytoplankton, however, is no longer multiplying as fast as it did in spring, and so there are fewer of the small creatures that feed on it. The animal life that is so evident in the pond now is composed largely of filter feeders, scavengers, and several levels of predatory consumers feeding upon an enormous amount of animal substance that got its start with the primary production by plants earlier in the year.

Shoreline plants continue to grow and to flourish. Almost all summer long, flowers along the shore lend their color and fragrance to the pond. They attract pollinating insects, some of which are caught by frogs, dragonflies, and other predators that lurk in the dense masses of emergent plants.

As summer passes, the water becomes dark with increased quantities of zooplankton and organic particles, and perhaps with soil particles washed from land during summer rains. You seldom see the larger animals that were so evident in early summer; they have laid their eggs and raised their broods. Frogs no longer call to one another. The markings of sunfish, shiners, and other fishes are not so vivid, and the colors of the smaller birds, such as redwings, do not seem so brilliant as they did in May and June. The leaves of spatterdock take on a battered, dry appearance, and a few of the emergent plants begin to wither in the August heat.

As September approaches, dodder flowers along the shore, conspicuous wherever it grows. It is one of the few parasitic seed plants, and it often attacks water willow, a common emergent. Vinelike, it winds its slender yellow stems around the stems of the water willow.

Dodder has no leaves to speak of, and it does not manufacture food by photosynthesis; instead it obtains nourishment from a host plant. Budding from the dodder stems are tiny extensions that penetrate the tough tissues of the water willow to the depth of the conducting vessels. With these stem extensions dodder removes food manufactured in the leaves of the host. Apparently it does the water willow little harm. The whole shoreline may appear to be covered by heavy yellow cobwebs in late summer, but there is always just as much water willow the next year.

The aquatic insect population is at its peak in late summer and early fall. Many of the insects that develop in water and leave as flying adults emerge at this time of year, occasionally filling the air in swarms. The emergence of mayflies earlier in the season is a remarkable phenomenon in some areas of the country, but it is of short duration. More flying insects leave the pond in the late summer than at any other time of year.

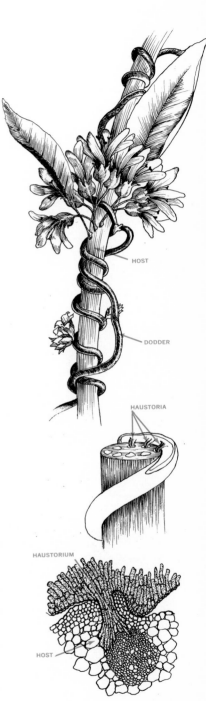

One of the strangest of the pond's shoreline plants is dodder, a leafless parasitic plant that cannot manufacture food of its own. Instead, dodder winds its way along the stems of such plants as water willow and sends out specialized structures called *haustoria*, which penetrate into the host plant and drain off a portion of its food substances. In July and August, dodder produces dense clusters of tiny whitish flowers. Dodder is an annual and dies in the fall; its seeds fall to the ground and pass the winter at the base of the host plant, where they germinate with the return of warm weather. Once the upward-groping seedlings have gained a grip on a host plant, they entirely break off contact with the soil.

A pond can be thought of as a sort of chemical factory receiving energy and raw materials from the outside world and, through a complex set of internal operations, manufacturing a variety of products, some of which return to the outside world. The principal source of energy is the sun, without whose light and heat the pond's "machinery" could not function. Raw materials come from a variety of sources: chemicals leach into the water from the soil (although the reverse may also occur); rain also washes in sediment and other materials from the land; the air furnishes oxygen and carbon dioxide; birds, mammals, and reptiles contribute their waste products and, sometimes, their dead bodies; leaves, pollen, and insects fall onto the surface and eventually are consumed; also a . . .

A pond loses food

The organisms that depart from a pond take away reserves of energy and nutrients contained in the organic matter in their bodies. Midges, for example, may be very small insects, but the millions that leave even a small pond during the course of a summer account for a considerable loss. And most departing insects are much larger than midges.

Larger animals, too, take organic material away from the pond. Frogs spend their tadpole days as primary consumers, browsing on algal coatings on plant stems and rock surfaces; but they grow quickly, leave the pond, and spend much of their time on land nearby. As long as waterfowl are present, they continually take organic matter from the pond; so do herons, ospreys, and kingfishers. Otters, muskrats, and raccoons regularly remove plant and animal food from the water and the shores.

A pond is a kind of sieve through which water passes

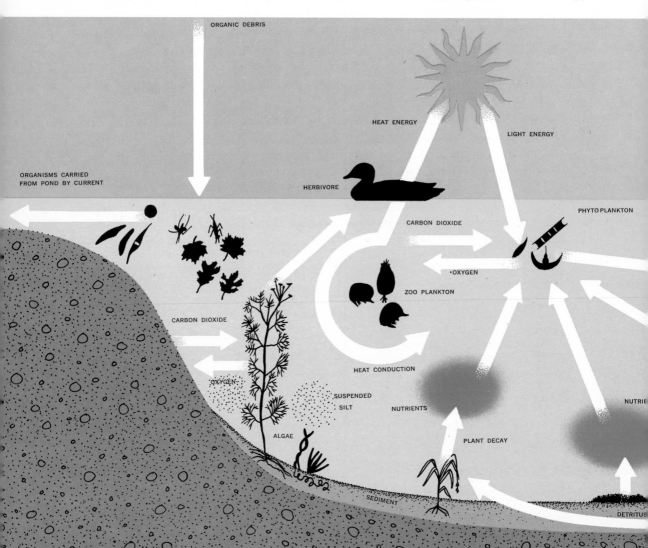

ORGANIC DEBRIS

HEAT ENERGY

LIGHT ENERGY

ORGANISMS CARRIED FROM POND BY CURRENT

HERBIVORE

PHYTO PLANKTON

CARBON DIOXIDE

·OXYGEN

ZOO PLANKTON

CARBON DIOXIDE

HEAT CONDUCTION

·OXYGEN·

SUSPENDED SILT

NUTRIENTS

NUTRIE

ALGAE

PLANT DECAY

SEDIMENT

DETRITUS

and from which energy, nutrients, and organic matter are constantly being extracted. But if it is to harbor a rich community of plants and animals year after year, it must take in as much as is taken out of it.

How food is restored

Some of the ways by which the pond is replenished have already been mentioned: leaves fall into it from trees; organic matter and mineral nutrients from the land are carried into it by streams and by surface run-off. Pollen is an important source of organic material. There are, in addition, some animal contributions, but not nearly enough to balance the loss. An occasional land mammal or bird dies and falls into the water; insects are trapped in the water film and either are devoured by pond animals or are decomposed on the bottom. Waste products from mammals, birds, snakes, and

. . . stream flowing into the pond can add all kinds of living organisms as well as organic and inorganic debris. All this input is acted upon in the pond's processes of production, consumption, and decomposition, and the end products comprise a community of plants and animals. Some of these leave the pond, as in the case of larval amphibians and insects that transform into land-dwelling adults; some are removed as food organisms, such as the plants and animals taken out by waterfowl, raccoons, and other nonaquatic consumers. If a stream flows out of the pond, part of its population leaves by that exit. In general, however, the pond achieves an approximate balance between its inputs and outputs, so that it remains a thriving, dynamic habitat year after year.

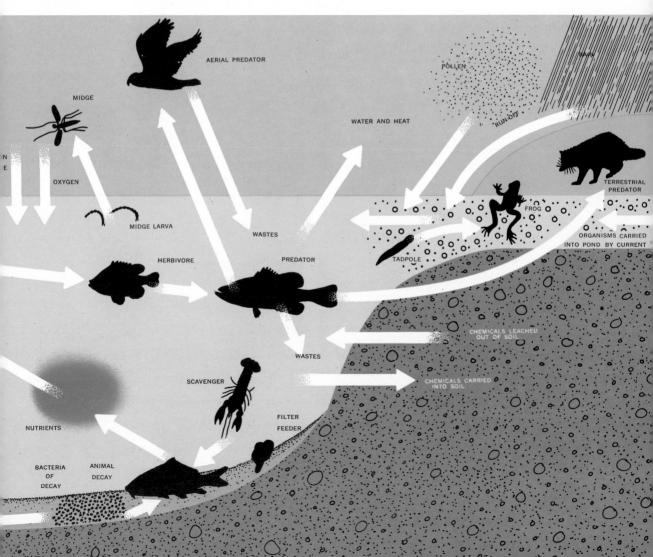

THE POND'S NIGHT RAIDERS

Visit any pond early in the morning, and
there is a good chance you will find fresh
tracks like the ones shown below—a sure
sign that a raccoon has been there during the
night. Or perhaps one of these agile
black-masked animals will put in an
appearance as you sit quietly by the shore
in the late dusk. With luck, you might even
see a mother coon with three or four
youngsters in tow, paddling quietly through
the water. Raccoons eat nearly anything, and
the pond offers good hunting for their fast,
dexterous paws: crayfish, shellfish, frogs, fish,
duck eggs, and young muskrats are all part
of the coon diet. But the animals are mainly
nocturnal, and the first light of dawn finds
them waddling back to their dens to doze
the day away.

The arrival of fall marks the
close of the pond year. Now
each one of the multitude of
living things that make their
home here—plant or animal,
large or small—must make its
arrangements to ensure the
continuity of its kind through
the long winter ahead. Some,
such as the beavers, will remain
somewhat active through the
cold months. Most of the birds
will migrate southward to
warmer climates. The reptiles
and amphibians will pass the
winter in hibernation. Many of
the smaller organisms will
simply perish with the coming
of the cold, but they will leave
behind cysts and reproductive
products such as eggs and seeds,
from which new generations
will arise when the spring sun
again stirs the pond to life.

frogs contribute a little. Creatures that lay their eggs in the pond add to its organic stores, but only to a slight degree, for the eggs are minute. The most important source of food for the pond community is the primary production of its green plants.

The chill of fall

By early fall the countryside around the pond is a riot of color. People take walks to admire the fall foliage, but how many notice the colors of the smaller plants of a pond? The delicate pink clusters of water smartweed flowers cover the advancing front of emergent vegetation; clusters of water willow flowers form islands of purple; the deep red flowers of spiked loosestrife rise above the low-lying emergents.

Beneath the pond's surface, the fresh-water sponges look sickly. During the winter they will disintegrate, but their cells already have produced thousands of tiny *gemmules*, protected sporelike bodies that can withstand the rigors of winter and start new colonies in the spring. *Pectinatella*, a bryozoan, or "moss animal," that lives in large gelatinous colonies, solves the problem of surviving in winter in a similar way, by producing tiny disk-shaped objects known as *statoblasts*. They become entangled in vegetation close to the surface, favorable places for next year's colonies to begin growing.

During the summer, *Hydra*, a little tentacled creature that feeds on zooplankton, reproduced mostly by budding new individuals from its trunk; but now it reproduces sexually, producing a few thick-walled eggs. Female rotifers are beginning to lay special winter eggs, after having produced great numbers of thin-walled summer eggs that invariably turned into more females, exact copies of their mothers. Many of the rotifers die, and certain species survive only in the safe winter eggs.

By now, spatterdock and other pond lilies are falling to pieces. Their fragments gradually filter down to the bottom and add to the organic blanket coating the mud. Leaves from the emergents blow off, and the stems dry out and wither, leaving only the rootstocks on low, protected stems to survive the winter. With every gust of wind, multitudes of

GEMMULE
(Spongilla lacustris)

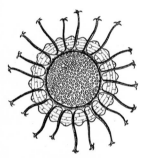

STATOBLAST
(Cristatella mucedo)

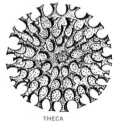

THECA
(Hydra littoralis)

88

leaves from the trees fringing the shoreline drift down into the water and are caught there. Some blow like miniature boats across the surface, but eventually they sink and become part of the rich sediment on the pond bottom.

The sun sinks a little lower in the sky each day, and the water cools, but not enough yet to hinder the growth of plankton. With so many nutrients entering the pond there may be another bloom of phytoplankton before the year is over, with a corresponding increase in zooplankton. But this late bloom will not equal that of the spring.

To migrate or to sleep

Suddenly you are aware that there are no more frogs about, and very few turtles. Only on sunny fall days do you find occasional painted turtles basking on shoreline logs, and with the first chill days they, too, are gone.

Turtles, snakes, frogs, and salamanders are not able to regulate their body temperatures like birds and mammals. They cannot cope with freezing temperatures and must hibernate. Water snakes generally find protected spots in old logs and under stones along the shore, and so do many of the salamanders. Their bodily processes slow down, and they become totally inactive. Frogs and turtles spend the winter under the mud at the bottom of a pond. Frogs have many blood vessels under their loose, moist skin, and while they hibernate they are able to absorb all the oxygen they need directly from the water. Turtles, with their watertight skin, have another means of obtaining oxygen. They inhale and exhale water through a large posterior opening, which serves also as an outlet for their excretory and reproductive systems. This cavity is extensively supplied with blood vessels and acts as a kind of gill.

The various ways in which plants survive the winter are less complex than those of the animals, but just as effective. Though the large leaves of water lilies die, the sizable stems and root systems live on in the bottom. This is the case with most emergents. Submerged plants such as waterweed and bladderwort produce either seeds or protected sprouts, which live through the winter after the rest of the plant has died. Algae remain somewhat active all year, even under the ice, or spend the winter as spores.

Perhaps more than most other aquatic habitats, the pond is responsive to the shifting seasons. The pond world is a world of extremes, and the plants and animals that populate it must endure these extremes or perish. In the spring, when conditions favor growth and proliferation, these activities are carried on with furious intensity. Summer may be a period of relatively easy living—or it may bring the threat of death through drought. Fall allows a brief renewed frenzy of growth in preparation for winter; winter brings the harshest trials of all. Yet despite the perils, the pond's community of living things thrives in wondrous variety and abundance.

The next four pages show a New Jersey pond during the four seasons: spring, summer, fall, and winter.

The icy grip of winter

Surviving the winter is never easy, and in a pond it is particularly difficult. A pond, with its relatively thin layer of water, quickly reflects atmospheric conditions. If the winter is exceptionally severe, pond organisms suffer along with their terrestrial cousins.

The pond is so shallow that once it cools off and freezes over, the temperature of the water beneath the ice is close to freezing. Only a few cold-blooded animals are at all active in this very cold water—fish, some insect larvae, amphipods and isopods, and burrowing worms. And except for an occasional star-nosed mole, very few warm-blooded animals are active in the pond. Beavers and muskrats build dens with underwater exits, but the chambers themselves are above the water level. Beavers occasionally venture from their lodges to get twigs from the stockpiles near their tunnel entrances, but muskrats may not emerge from their lodges for weeks on end.

As long as ice and snow cover the pond, aquatic animals face an ever-present danger: death by suffocation. The ice-covered water of the pond is sealed off from the atmosphere. The thin layer of air trapped under the ice is sufficient to replenish the bubbles carried by aquatic beetles, for their demands are slight at this time of year. And unless the ice lasts for many weeks and months, most pond animals with gills are able to survive, for their requirements are low as long as they remain inactive. But some of the animals are not so tolerant as others. You may find fish frozen in the ice; they probably died from lack of oxygen, floated up to the ice, and were enclosed. If ice covers the pond for long periods of time, even more aquatic animals may perish. If it thickens and reaches the bottom, almost all will die.

The winter plankton population, though greatly reduced, is active as long as some water remains. It consists primarily of a few diatoms, rotifers, and crustaceans. One small cladoceran water flea, *Daphnia*, has a curious response to winter.

In common with many other planktonic organisms, successive generations of the water flea *Daphnia* respond to seasonal changes in temperature with changes in body shape. The warm water of summer is less dense than the cold winter water and therefore is more difficult to stay afloat in; during the summer *Daphnia* develops a pointed head that increases its surface area and serves as an aid in flotation. This modification disappears as the water in the fall becomes cooler and therefore more dense.

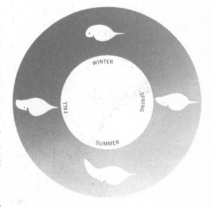

An unusually severe winter can take a heavy toll of the pond's population: a prolonged covering of ice and snow acts as a suffocating blanket beneath which animals die for want of oxygen.

95

In the course of a year, the *Daphnia* population in a pond goes through many generations. The individuals produced in the winter have rounded heads, while those produced in the summer have heads extended into helmetlike points. This seasonal difference in shape is explained by the changing density of the water. In summer, when the water is warm and less dense, the greater surface area provided by the pointed head is an advantage. It helps the water flea to stay afloat near the surface. In winter, when the water is more dense and planktonic organisms float more easily, such flotation devices are not necessary.

Once a pond freezes over, further temperature changes are unlikely. The bottom generally is a couple of degrees above freezing—warm enough for a few organisms to remain active. Decomposition in the thick layers of leaves and organic sediments slows down during winter, but it will increase enormously as the water warms in spring.

There may be little to see on the surface of a pond in winter. If ice does not cover it completely, a few birds will feed in the open water. Often herring gulls come many miles from the sea to feed in the quieter waters of inland ponds, and their quarrelsome mewing can be heard some distance away. All winter long you can watch mallards and mergansers paddling about in open water and standing on the margins of the ice far out in the pond. The occasional remaining heron may be forced to compete with the gulls for food, perhaps even by robbing them of freshly caught fish.

Life is now at its lowest ebb in the pond. All is quiet. Yet beneath the surface and along the shore lies enormous promise: dormant living things are packed millions to the cubic inch. All that is required is a little time and a warming sun, and the life of the pond will burst forth again.

Clutched in the numbing grip of winter, the pond is dormant and inert, but nevertheless infused with the promise of boundless vitality that awaits only the coming of spring.

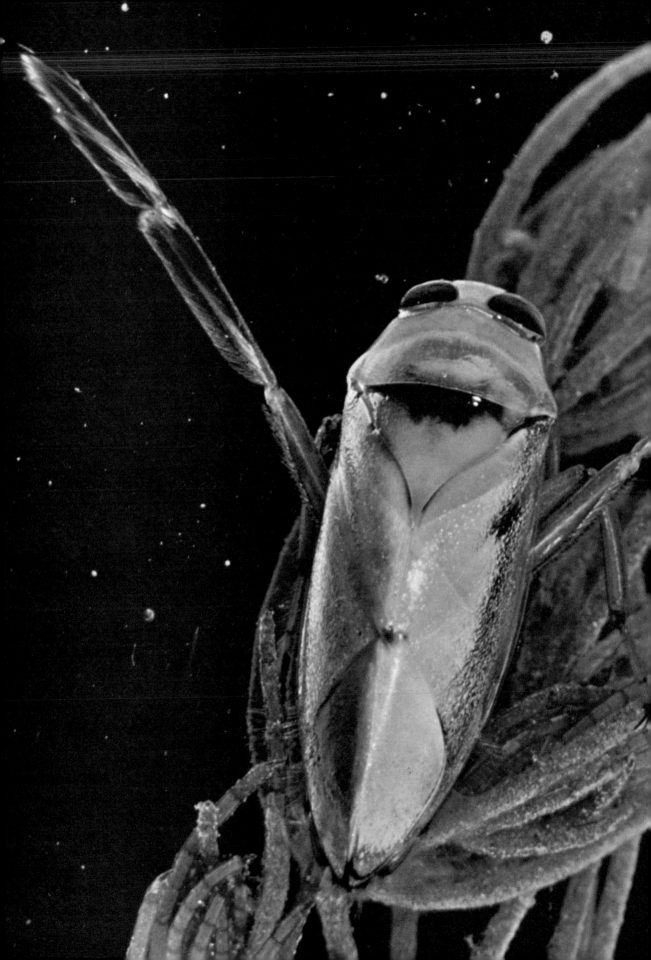

Living
in Water

Life probably began in the shallow coastal waters of ancient seas two billion or more years ago. There, perhaps with lightning and ultraviolet light as energy sources, simple molecules were bound together into complex structures that eventually became capable of making more of their own kind. In their food habits, these first primitive forms of life resembled animals more closely than plants. But in time certain organisms developed the ability to manufacture their own food using light energy. They were the first plants.

Over a period of millions of years living organisms entered bays and rivers, and gradually invaded fresh water. The transition from salt water to fresh was not easy, however, and fresh-water organisms can be looked upon as highly specialized life forms that have made successful adjustments to a difficult habitat. To this day, ponds, lakes, and rivers contain far fewer kinds of animals than the oceans, and some major groups of marine animals—starfish and arrowworms, for example—have no relatives in fresh water.

What is so difficult about moving from salt water to fresh water? An organism that lives in the sea maintains a delicate balance between the salts in its body and those in the surrounding water. When it enters fresh water, this balance is upset, and its tissues rapidly take in dangerous quantities of water. To survive in fresh water, a species must possess either a tough, waterproof skin or organs that can get rid of excess water.

If you compare the internal organs of a marine fish with those of a fresh-water fish, you will notice a difference at once: the fresh-water fish's kidneys, which are used largely for water regulation, are large, while the salt-water fish's

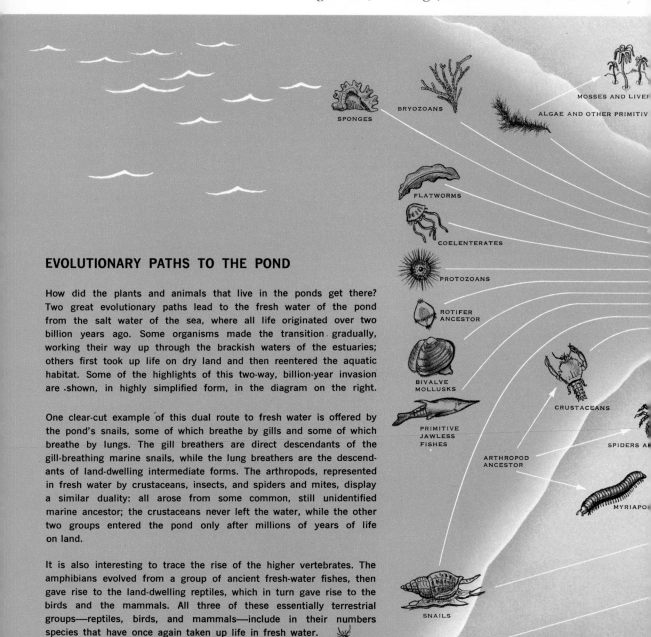

EVOLUTIONARY PATHS TO THE POND

How did the plants and animals that live in the ponds get there? Two great evolutionary paths lead to the fresh water of the pond from the salt water of the sea, where all life originated over two billion years ago. Some organisms made the transition gradually, working their way up through the brackish waters of the estuaries; others first took up life on dry land and then reentered the aquatic habitat. Some of the highlights of this two-way, billion-year invasion are shown, in highly simplified form, in the diagram on the right.

One clear-cut example of this dual route to fresh water is offered by the pond's snails, some of which breathe by gills and some of which breathe by lungs. The gill breathers are direct descendants of the gill-breathing marine snails, while the lung breathers are the descendants of land-dwelling intermediate forms. The arthropods, represented in fresh water by crustaceans, insects, and spiders and mites, display a similar duality: all arose from some common, still unidentified marine ancestor; the crustaceans never left the water, while the other two groups entered the pond only after millions of years of life on land.

It is also interesting to trace the rise of the higher vertebrates. The amphibians evolved from a group of ancient fresh-water fishes, then gave rise to the land-dwelling reptiles, which in turn gave rise to the birds and the mammals. All three of these essentially terrestrial groups—reptiles, birds, and mammals—include in their numbers species that have once again taken up life in fresh water.

SPONGES

BRYOZOANS

MOSSES AND LIVER

ALGAE AND OTHER PRIMITIV

FLATWORMS

COELENTERATES

PROTOZOANS

ROTIFER ANCESTOR

BIVALVE MOLLUSKS

PRIMITIVE JAWLESS FISHES

ARTHROPOD ANCESTOR

CRUSTACEANS

SPIDERS AN

MYRIAPO

SNAILS

kidneys are small. Even one-celled fresh-water animals have developed water-regulating devices. The protozoans *Paramecium* and *Amoeba*, for example, have contractile vacuoles within their cytoplasm that discharge excess water; their marine relatives lack these little devices.

Fresh-water fishes, crustaceans, many other types of animals, and phytoplankton evolved directly from marine forms without ever leaving water. But many aquatic animals and most aquatic plants reinvaded a watery environment after first developing into land-dwelling forms. The emergent

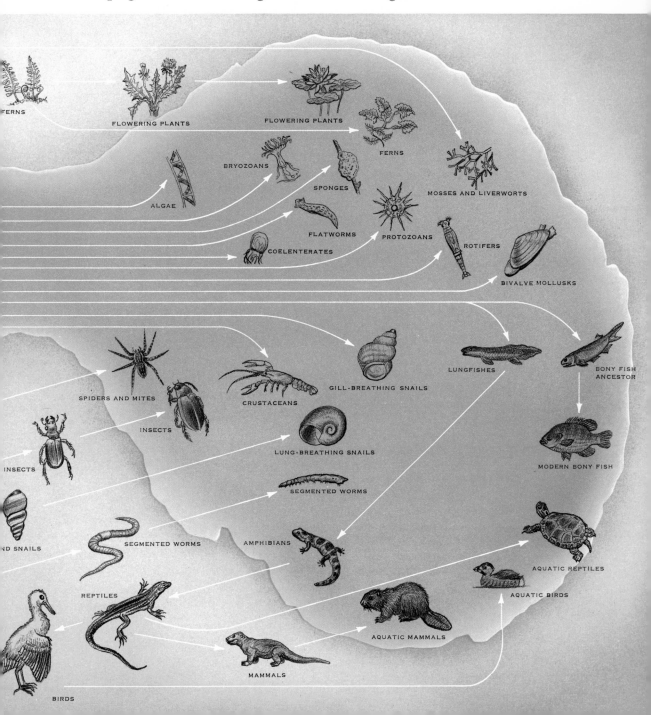

FERNS

FLOWERING PLANTS   FLOWERING PLANTS

FERNS

BRYOZOANS

SPONGES

MOSSES AND LIVERWORTS

ALGAE

FLATWORMS   PROTOZOANS

COELENTERATES

ROTIFERS

BIVALVE MOLLUSKS

LUNGFISHES   BONY FISH ANCESTOR

SPIDERS AND MITES   GILL-BREATHING SNAILS

CRUSTACEANS

INSECTS

LUNG-BREATHING SNAILS

INSECTS

MODERN BONY FISH

SEGMENTED WORMS

ND SNAILS   SEGMENTED WORMS   AMPHIBIANS

AQUATIC REPTILES

REPTILES   AQUATIC BIRDS

AQUATIC MAMMALS

MAMMALS

BIRDS

plants, the floaters, and the submerged seed plants are all descended from forms that originally developed on land.

Plants that live in water

Not including any of the algae, the mosses, or the ferns, more than twelve hundred species of plants are found in or near fresh water in the United States, and most of these grow in ponds. Each species is associated with a certain zone and has structural adaptations that enable it to live there successfully.

The roots of aquatic plants generally are small and have few root hairs compared with those of land plants. The major function of a land plant's root hairs is to obtain water and nutrients. Since aquatic plants are surrounded by water containing dissolved nutrients, they need relatively few root hairs. But although aquatic plants can easily get water and nutrients, they may have difficulty in obtaining the oxygen their cells need to break down food. The roots of some emergent plants develop special oxygen-acquiring tissues that reach out into the air. Most submerged plants get oxygen in another way. They use oxygen produced in photosynthesis, storing the excess in the airspaces of their stems and drawing on it at night and on dark days.

The leaves of submerged plants usually are long and so thin that their green cells can easily absorb carbon dioxide, which they need for photosynthesis, directly from the surrounding water. The leaves of plants that grow closer to the surface may be wider and thicker, and those of floating plants almost invariably are very broad and filled with airspaces. The leaves of emergent plants resemble those of land plants, and may be spear-shaped, triangular, rounded, or any of a variety of other shapes. Some emergent plants have two types of leaves, aerial leaves growing above the water and submerged leaves growing under the water. These are distinctly different in shape, possibly because the submerged leaves do not get enough food to develop fully. If the submerged leaves did get enough food, they would resemble the aerial leaves. The aerial leaves differ from the submerged leaves in structure as well as in shape. Aerial leaves have stomates, and their inner tissues are composed of tall columnar cells. Most submerged leaves have neither stomates nor columnar cells.

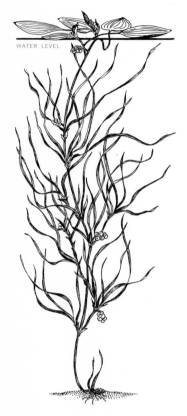

WATER LEVEL

An aquatic plant often exhibits two types of leaves, those that grow beneath the water and those that either float on or thrust above the surface. The pondweed shown here displays this differentiation. Its underwater leaves are tough, pliant, and finely divided, offering little resistance to water currents. The floating leaves, on the other hand, are broad and raftlike, exposing a large surface to the sun and providing a firm base for the aerial flower stalks.

102

Pluck a handful of submerged water lily stalks. You will find them slippery, for they are coated with mucus. This coating probably discourages animals from eating the soft tissues underneath and protects the stems when currents cause the plants to rub against each other. If you look under the water surface, you will see a tangled jungle of stems, yet seldom will you find evidence that one stem has injured another.

There are two basic types of aquatic plant stems: those that support leaves out of water and those that act simply as anchor lines and conducting tubes. The stems of many erect emergent plants have water-conducting vessels in bundles arranged circularly in their outside layers. These conducting vessels are bound closely together with fibers that provide support for the stems. But submerged plants are buoyed by water, and they do not need support. Their relatively weak stems are filled with airspaces, which help them to float. In many plants the vessels that conduct water and dissolved minerals upward are situated in the centers of the stems rather than in the outside layers.

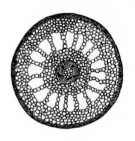

The stem structure of many aquatic plants, including the water milfoil shown here, differs from that of most land plants in being nearly devoid of woody supporting structures. Instead, the typical aquatic stem contains a system of airspaces which serve two purposes. First, they buoy up the stem, holding the plant upright in the water. Second, they serve as a reservoir for surplus oxygen produced by the plant's photosynthesis and utilized in its metabolic processes.

Plants and more plants

If you were to compare several photographs of a pond taken over a period of ten or fifteen years, you might be astonished at how fast the plants growing along the shoreline move outward into the water. Water willow loops its way out into open water by means of stems that take root in the bottom mud. Spike rushes and reed grasses send out thin stems that creep over the bottom, well below the water level. The stems and roots of smartweed are almost indistinguishable from one another; rootlets stick out into the water at frequent intervals along submerged portions of the stems. Thus the open bottom of the pond is constantly being invaded by a maze of stems that quickly take root and send up branches to the surface. This form of reproduction, which does not involve sexual methods, is known as *vegetative reproduction*.

The waterweed *Anacharis*, a submerged plant often used in aquariums, provides one of the most unusual examples of vegetative reproduction. In the fall, a special terminal bud appears at the tip of each stalk. It is simply a compact bit of stem with tightly compressed leaves. With the approach of

WATER LEVEL

103

winter, the body of the plant dies and rots away, but the terminal bud drops to the bottom. In spring, it begins to grow, and soon there is a new stalk of waterweed. Water milfoil and bladderwort survive the winter in much the same way as waterweed. If a stalk of any one of these plants is broken in half during the growing season, each part continues to grow. Thus large beds of waterweed, milfoil, or bladderwort develop in shallow parts of a pond.

Flowers in the water

Water lilies are the best known aquatic flowers. A white water lily floating in the dark waters of a quiet pond is a lovely sight. The flower of the yellow water lily, or spatterdock, is not so attractive. It is a massive and heavy structure, with an enlarged female portion on top and the male parts deep inside a cup of petals. The flowers of many other aquatic plants are small and unimpressive to the naked eye, although they may be colorful and complex when you look at them under a magnifying glass.

The flowers of most aquatic plants, even those of otherwise submerged plants such as pondweeds, must be exposed to the air so that they can be pollinated by wind or by insects. Only hornwort and a few other species develop flowers that open underwater and are fertilized by water-borne pollen.

The flowers of the tiny floating duckweed and watermeal are the strangest in the pond. They are merely exceedingly small eruptions of the plant's surface, and they do not seem to be very important to the survival of these minute plants. For the most part, duckweed and watermeal simply bud off new individuals, some of which survive the winter.

The waxlike flowers of the white water lily open when the morning sun strikes them and close up again in the afternoon. The flowers and the leathery pads, both about six inches in diameter, are true floaters; their long, slender stalks serve to anchor them to the plant's buried rootstock. The lily's fruits produce floating seeds which are eaten by ducks and other water birds; beavers and muskrats feed upon the foliage. Common in ponds and other quiet waters throughout the eastern United States, the lily produces its fragrant white (and occasionally pink) flowers from June through September.

The simpler plants

Mosses, liverworts, and ferns are at times found in or near ponds, although they are seldom abundant. The only mosses of great importance in ponds are the sphagnum mosses mentioned earlier. Liverworts are common along shaded pond shores, and some species actually float on the surface of quiet waters.

Pepperwort or water fern can at times completely cover exposed shores. Water velvet, *Azolla,* a member of the fern family, floats on the surface of sheltered pond waters in the company of duckweed and watermeal. Its reddish lobed leaves stretch out in rosette patterns, contrasting handsomely with its bright green companions. On the wet banks of a pond you may find the large royal fern, with its conspicuous brown spore-bearing leaflets rising in the center of a spray of green fronds.

The smallest of all

Members of the phytoplankton are extremely numerous. All of these are algae—blue-green, green, or yellow-brown. The blue-greens are exceedingly primitive plants that are not always bluish-green at all, but may be brown, reddish, or even black. At times they multiply, or bloom, in such great abundance that poisons are set free into the pond when they decay. Though there is no evidence that these poisons are dangerous to humans, people are not inclined to go near a pond when a blue-green bloom is in progress. The water is frothy and discolored and often has a foul smell heightened by the odors of decaying fish that suffocated for lack of oxygen. These blooms usually occur in small ponds when the water has been warmed by sunlight and contains an abundance of nutrients. They may have a profound effect upon the community of plants and animals in a pond, but they are seldom predictable and seldom preventable.

Perhaps the best known blue-green in a pond is not planktonic at all, but a shoreline and shallow-water plant. It is *Oscillatoria,* a filament of many small cells that moves with a gliding motion, interrupted by peculiar jerks. This motion is caused by a film of slime that flows slowly over the outside of the whole filament. When abundant, *Oscillatoria* forms a blackish scum on wet shoreline mud.

Green algae are not always numerous as members of the plankton, although they may exist in great masses of filaments in the shallowest parts of a pond. There are hundreds of species of filamentous green algae. Two basic types, *Spirogyra* and *Oedogonium*, are familiar to most biology students. Some of the others are more complex. *Chaetophora*, an intricately branched form that grows in great abundance on solid surfaces in smaller ponds during the summer, is an important source of food for browsing first-order consumers. At times the water in small and quiet ponds suddenly turns green with immense numbers of *Euglena*, a single-celled organism that is claimed by both botanists and zoologists because it possesses features of both plants and animals. A few days later the water clears, just as suddenly, leaving relatively few of the creatures.

A planktonic alga of greater importance to the biological economy of a pond is the diatom, a microscopic one-celled plant with yellowish-brown cytoplasm enclosed in a clear glasslike case. The transparent case, composed largely of silica, is formed of two halves that fit together like the lid and bottom of a box. In some species thin streamers of cytoplasm flow along the crack between lid and bottom, causing the entire cell to move slowly and evenly.

Some pond diatoms are linked together into chains, and the cells of *Asterionella* form star-shaped patterns. To the pond watcher, blooms of *Asterionella* in the early months of the year are harbingers of spring, much as skunk cabbage is along the marshy shores. *Asterionella* is so abundant in some ponds that the water becomes yellowish and opaque.

Like living asterisks, clusters of *Asterionella* diatoms spangle the pond's early spring plankton community, often in enormous abundance. Each "ray" of the cluster is a complete, independent plant encased in a two-part silica shell about a thirty-second of an inch long, just big enough to distinguish with the naked eye. Despite the small size of the individual plants, diatoms and other algae are of vital importance in the ecology of the pond.

If you find neatly cut lengths of cattail stalks or other plant parts littering the pond's surface, or mussel shells scattered on the shore, chances are good that muskrats are present. Although largely vegetarian, muskrats also feed upon various small invertebrates, and in turn they are preyed upon by minks, otters, owls, hawks, and, most seriously, by man, who takes the rodent for its fur and its meat.

Animals that take to water

All animals that live in ponds must be able to swim, or at least to move about in, or on top of, the water. Each major animal group has found its own way, but even within one group there is much variation. Among the insects, for example, there are divers, crawlers, burrowers, skaters, and so on. And among the vertebrates, too, there are a variety of capable swimmers, divers, and burrowers.

The beaver and the muskrat are well-known primary consumers, still abundant in some parts of the country even though they are trapped for their pelts. Both build sizable houses, and both are excellent swimmers and divers.

The otter is probably the most skillful and graceful of all fresh-water mammals, exceeding nearly all other animals of pond and stream in swimming ability. An otter will catch muskrats without difficulty. It also eats crayfish, fish, frogs, salamanders, insects, and occasionally waterfowl. While it is unlikely that you will have the good fortune to watch otters swim and play, much has been written about them, and there are fine films showing their agile underwater maneuvering.

The star-nosed mole, unlike its cousin the common mole,

108

lives in wet soil along the shores of ponds and marshes. Its burrows may extend out under a pond and actually lead into it. A star-nosed mole is a fine swimmer and preys upon small fish and also crayfish, aquatic insects, and a variety of other pond invertebrates. It is one of the few mammals that is active in the water all year, and it even swims under the ice in search of food.

Although the pied-billed grebe inhabits ponds throughout North America, you are unlikely to see one at close range. It is a timid bird, and dives or ducks under the water instantly, long before an unsuspecting human visitor has a chance to see what it is. The grebe spends much of its time in the heavy vegetation at the edge of the pond, where it feeds on small fish and other aquatic animals. It swims effortlessly underwater, pursuing its prey, for long periods of time. On land it is helpless and cannot take to the air, as it does from water, because its legs and webbed feet are placed far back on its body.

Nearly all the turtles that live in a pond have very large webbed hind feet, which are efficient paddles for swim-

Sleek, playful, and incomparably agile in the water, the otters are the most thoroughly aquatic of all the fresh-water mammals. They are confirmed meat eaters: muskrats, young beavers, fish, shellfish, frogs, turtles, snakes, earthworms, crayfish, and water birds are all part of their diet. Overhunting by fur trappers has greatly reduced our otter populations, and though otters are still widespread, they are now seldom seen.

ming. The front feet, with their long claws, are not heavily webbed and are used mainly for tearing apart food and crawling along the bottom.

These aquatic reptiles are more skillful in the water than their cumbersome shapes would suggest, for they are streamlined and muscular and are able to stay underwater for long periods of time. They are very timid and seldom allow you to approach them; a large red-bellied terrapin basking on a log will slip into the water when you are drifting silently in a canoe a hundred yards away. Some turtles, such as the musk turtle and the snapping turtle, seldom leave the water even to sun themselves, but females of all species climb the banks of the pond in the spring to lay their eggs in the soil.

There are only a few thoroughly aquatic amphibians in our ponds. Bullfrogs and green frogs are in the water most of the time, but the slender spotted newts, with their large finned tails, are even more committed to an aquatic life. Spotted newts go through a rather complex life cycle. Their eggs are fastened singly to stems and leaves of aquatic plants, and the larvae that emerge have external gills and develop as truly aquatic forms. Later, they lose their gills and crawl out on land, becoming for a while land forms known as red efts. When they mature, after two or three years, they return to the water, develop finned tails again, and live in the water from then on—but with lungs, not gills.

LARVAE

RED EFTS

SPOTTED NEWT

THE POND'S LIVING FOSSILS

Turtles are an exceedingly ancient group of animals, having evolved from a primitive land-dwelling reptile some 200 million years ago—long before the first dinosaurs roamed the earth. That the turtles have so successfully stood the test of time speaks well for their unique boxlike body armor, into which they retire when danger threatens. A variety of turtles make their homes in ponds. For the most part shy and mild-mannered, these placid creatures reach maturity in three to five years and may live for fifty years or even longer. Given intelligent care, many species make interesting and hardy pets.

Like many turtles, the red-bellied terrapin spends much of its time basking in the sun—often on a log or rock, but never far from deep water, into which it scrambles at the slightest disturbance. Sunbathing increases the rate of the turtles' metabolism, discourages the growth of algae on their shells, and helps control external parasites.

The chicken turtle (left), perhaps so named for the succulence of its flesh, is a common inhabitant of ponds in the southern Atlantic and Gulf states. Its shell may reach a length of ten inches, but individuals of about half that size are more usual. Even the most thoroughly aquatic of the turtles give evidence of their terrestrial ancestry when, like this red-eared turtle (right), they come ashore to lay their eggs in nests scooped out of loose soil, sand, or decaying vegetation.

A pond turtle's special adaptations to its habitat include elevated nostrils that allow it to take a breath at the surface with a minimum of exposure; eyes set well forward on its head, giving it partial binocular vision with which to judge distances accurately; and a sharp, bony beak and powerfully clawed forefeet for handling a wide variety of foods, both animal and vegetable.

To swim like a fish

Pond fish are not powerful swimmers like those of rivers or oceans, for they have no great distances to cover or strong currents to oppose.

How does a fish swim? It appears to push itself forward by wagging its tail fin from side to side. However, a fish deprived of its tail in an accident continues to swim.

Perhaps the best way of understanding a fish's swimming technique is to think of ice-skating. When you go in a straight line across the ice, you leave behind marks from your skates that are about forty-five degrees from your line of travel. In other words, you propel yourself forward by thrusting laterally, first to one side and then to the other. If you were to take a series of still photographs of a fish swimming in a straight line, its body (not its tail fin) would be shown flexing back and forth like a spring. A motion picture would reveal waves of muscular contraction moving down the body toward the rear, first on one side and then the other. The fish is actually pushing itself through the water much as a skater propels himself over the ice, with its

SWIMMERS OF THE POND

Water creatures live in a medium that buoys them up and more or less cancels the tug of gravity. Their appendages are largely relieved of the task of supporting body weight and can be devoted primarily to feeding and swimming. To move forward, a land animal must push backward against the ground and a flier must push backward against the air. Similarly, an aquatic animal moves forward by pushing backward against the water. There are many ways of doing this, some of which are shown at the right.

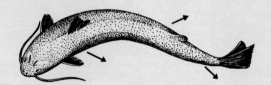

A fish moves forward by sending waves of muscular contractions down its body so that at any one time three or four pressure points (*arrows*) push backward against the water. The fins are used primarily for steering and braking.

The leech (seen here from the side) swims in the manner of a fish, with wavelike ripples traveling along the length of its body. But whereas the fish undulates from side to side, the leech undulates up and down.

head proceeding forward in a straight line. At any one time, a fish has three or four pressure points pushing against the water. An eel would have quite a few more, and a water snake even more than the eel.

The tail fin does aid in propulsion. The other fins are for the most part stabilizers, except when the fish is hovering quietly over the bottom; then the paired pelvic and pectoral fins may actually move the fish backward or forward, or keep it steady in a slight current. Most fish are weightless underwater; that is, their weight is balanced with an internal gas-filled bladder that serves as a kind of balloon. Bottom-dwelling fish, such as the Johnny darter, do not have swim bladders; their weight keeps them resting on the bottom.

If you should see an animal a few inches long swimming rapidly by waving its body up and down, rather than from side to side like a fish, it is one of the large leeches. Many kinds of leeches, not all of which are parasitic, are found in fresh water. Some feed on dead animal material in the bottom sediments. Others attach themselves to turtles or to fishes' fins, but one, the black horseleech, does attach itself to mammals when they come down to drink.

The diving beetle *Dytiscus* propels itself with very rapid oarlike strokes of its hind legs. On the power stroke (upper leg) the leg sweeps in a wide arc; on the recovery stroke (lower leg) the leg travels close to the body.

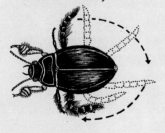

The larvae of certain dragonflies, in addition to crawling along the bottom, swim by a form of jet propulsion. The larva slowly draws water into its rectal gill chamber, then violently expels it and rockets forward through the water.

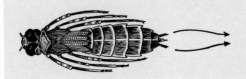

The backswimmer, like the diving beetle, uses its hind legs as oars. But because it is buoyant and its legs move relatively slowly, it travels along in a series of arcs, moving forward and downward on the power stroke and floating upward during the recovery stroke.

This midge larva is typical of the many aquatic wrigglers: it moves jerkily through the water by curling its body into a tight circle and then snapping it straight. Primarily a drifter, the larva only rarely resorts to swimming.

The diving beetle

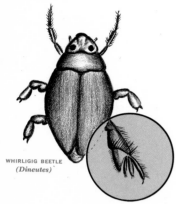

WHIRLIGIG BEETLE
(Dineutes)

DIVING BEETLE
(Dytiscus)

Both the whirligig beetle *Dineutes* and the diving beetle *Dytiscus* are powerful swimmers, with the third pair of legs modified to serve as strong oars, but the two insects differ in the form this adaptation takes. The hind legs of *Dineutes* are equipped with flat plates that function much like the flight feathers of birds: as the legs thrust backward in the power stroke, the plates overlap to form a solid paddle; on the recovery stroke, the plates open like a Venetian blind and offer little resistance to the water. The hind legs of *Dytiscus*, by contrast, are studded with long bristles which stand out to form a paddle on the power stroke, and which collapse and lie close to the leg on the recovery stroke.

Among the insects there are all kinds of swimmers, most of them very rapid and so elusive that even careful observation fails to tell how they move about. Only in recent years have biologists been able to understand precisely how they swim.

The body of *Dytiscus*, an inch-and-a-half-long diving beetle, is almost perfectly streamlined and closely approaches the ideal teardrop shape. When the diving beetle swims powerfully straight forward, the water separates around its body, flows smoothly over it, and rejoins at the rear with very little turbulence. Actually *Dytiscus* is more stable in the water than a perfect teardrop, for its underside is flattened, and it swims with its head slightly up. In this position it has the "lift" of an airplane wing or the vane of a hydrofoil boat.

Dytiscus moves forward by means of the strong oarlike thrusts of its hind, or third, pair of legs, which are controlled by powerful muscles. Each of these legs has a wide fringe of stiff hairs that stick outward to form a paddle blade when the leg is being thrust backward but lie close to the leg while it is pulled forward for the next stroke. Measurements made with a European diving beetle have shown the importance of the hairs: they account for sixty-eight percent of the total thrust generated by the leg. Without such hairs, the beetle would be neither a very skillful swimmer nor a very rapid one.

The whirligig *Gyrinus*, another beetle commonly found on the surface of ponds, has similar swimming abilities. But instead of bristles, it has a number of small flat blades that overlap and form a paddle with the power stroke but separate like a Venetian blind with the recovery stroke. Despite their flatness these blades are not so effective for diving as the bristles of *Dytiscus*, but they seem to be excellent for surface swimming. To see them, you would have to examine a captive specimen, for when one is swimming the legs beat approximately sixty times a second, far too fast for the eye to follow them.

As diving beetles submerge, they carry air under their wing covers and on the tips of their abdomens, and if they do not grab the bottom or a submerged plant with their front legs, they bob up to the surface like corks. They spend much of their time underwater, and are adept at chasing

The smoothly streamlined body and powerful fringed hind legs of the diving beetle *Dytiscus* make it one of the most accomplished of swimming insects. Snails, insects, crustaceans, and even tadpoles and small fish are among the victims of this voracious underwater predator. *Dytiscus* makes a good subject for aquarium study; fed on bits of raw meat, it will live two to three years in captivity.

down swimming prey, maneuvering with great skill until the victim is captured.

Other insect swimmers

Two rather similar kinds of insects, backswimmers and water boatmen, are familiar pond insects. Both have long, oarlike hind legs sticking far out on both sides of their bodies.

The backswimmer is buoyant, but its leg movements are far slower than those of the beetles. It moves in a looping path, alternately fast and slow. Each stroke of its legs drives the backswimmer forward and downward, but the insect slows down and begins to rise as the recovery stroke is made. When it kicks its legs rapidly, it dives; when it kicks more slowly, it swims toward the surface. It preys on other insects and even small fish, and can give you a sharp stinging bite if you handle it carelessly.

The water boatman is similar but smaller. It feeds mostly on fine decayed plant material, or detritus, which it collects with its small front legs. The second pair of legs serves as a rudder and a grasping organ for clinging to the bottom. Water boatmen are strong fliers and migrate from pond to pond with ease.

If you should temporarily keep a few water boatmen in a dry container, do not be surprised if you hear a chirping sound. A male water boatman can make sounds, possibly

Each of the water boatman's three pairs of legs has its own specialized function: the short and delicately fringed forelegs sift through the mud for the bits of plant debris that form the insect's chief food; the long, clawed middle legs anchor the buoyant creature to the bottom; the hind legs serve as oars which propel the boatman through the water.

for mating purposes, by rubbing its front legs against a scraper on the side of its head.

The elongated larvae of mayflies, damselflies, caddisflies, and midges swim either by strong movements of their widened tails or by snakelike body motions. Some dragonfly nymphs shoot jets of water from their abdomens, thus pushing themselves forward at speeds of almost two feet a second. If a land-dwelling rove beetle, *Stenus*, falls into a pond, it secretes a fluid that lowers the surface tension of the water in front of its head. It is then propelled forward rapidly across the surface by physical forces of the water.

Chaoborus, the phantom midge larva, is one of the few insect members of the zooplankton. During the daylight hours it swims about just above the bottom, but at night it migrates upward near the surface. Except for its eyes and two pairs of gas-filled sacs, its transparent body is almost invisible. The volume of the gas sacs is controlled by chemical secretions resulting from nervous stimulation: when the sacs are compressed, the insect sinks; when they are expanded, it rises. The air sacs of *Chaoborus* are a vestige of the tracheal, or air-tube, system of all insects, but in this midge larva the system no longer is connected with the outside. This may also allow the phantom midge larva to live for a short while in waters containing very little oxygen.

Chaoborus makes very rapid jerking movements which propel it in a vertical plane. Aided by a "fin" of feathered bristles on its tail, it moves so strenuously that it can jump completely out of a shallow dish of water.

The phantom midge larva's two pairs of silvery air sacs act as organs of equilibrium, adjusting the half-inch-long creature's buoyancy so that it can rise, sink, or hover in the water. Twitching movements of the bristled tail, as well as movements of the entire body, propel the larva through the water in its pursuit of copepods and other members of the animal plankton.

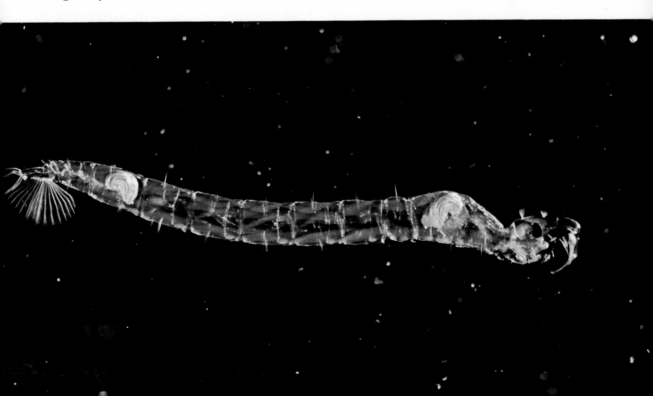

Jellyfish and crustaceans

If you are interested in how animals swim, you can find dozens of species to study in any pond. In addition to fish and insects, there are crustaceans, protozoans, and even jellyfish. It is a little-known fact that fresh waters can support a small jellyfish, *Craspedacusta,* which is about the size of a dime. It is found in reservoirs, water-filled quarries, and ponds; some years it is abundant, and other years not one can be found.

Craspedacusta actually is a *medusa,* which is an alternate generation of a small bottom-dwelling hydroid, even more rarely seen. The medusa swims with rhythmic pulsations, rather like the opening and closing of an umbrella. It rises to the surface, stops pulsating, turns over, and drifts downward with tentacles outstretched. Each tentacle has hun-

2

1

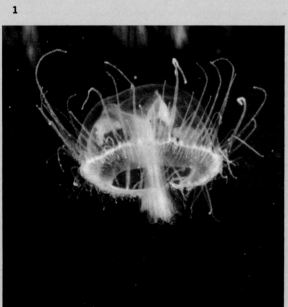

dreds of microscopic stinging capsules arranged in clusters. As the animal sinks, it paralyzes and collects planktonic animals that brush against the tentacles. When the jellyfish gets close to the bottom, it turns right side up and swims to the surface again.

Some animals migrate vertically through the water without swimming at all. Pond snails and *Hydra* secrete gas bubbles that carry them to the surface after they release their hold on the bottom. Once at the surface, these creatures crawl on the surface film, which to them is a firm ceiling.

Planktonic crustaceans, whether they are copepods or water fleas (cladocerans), generally swim by beating their legs or waving their antennae. They are so small that they displace very little water and produce very little friction as they push their way forward. As a result, it takes relatively little effort for them to move rapidly and for great distances through the water.

Rhythmic contractions of its thumbnail-sized body send this fresh-water jellyfish upward through the water by gentle jet propulsion (1) Reaching the surface (2), it turns over and sinks to the bottom again (3), with tentacles outstretched. Then it rights itself (4) and begins a new trip to the surface. It eats tiny creatures captured and killed by its stinging tentacles. Although jellyfish are abundant in the sea, the species shown here, *Craspedacusta*, is the sole member of the group to be found in the fresh waters of North America.

3

4

Microscopic swimmers

The world of protozoans, or one-celled animals, is one that you cannot explore without a microscope. But if you are fortunate enough to have one, it is a world that will hold your attention for hours and perhaps for the rest of your life.

Flagellates use their long, whiplike flagella in several ways. Some species have flagella that extend forward and create vortexes which draw them forward. Other species have flagella that trail behind and whip back and forth, acting like sculling oars. An accessory flagellum may extend in a groove around the animal, causing it to spin on its axis.

Ciliates have many rows of small coordinated hairlike structures, or *cilia*, which beat together rhythmically. Within their microscopic bodies are complex patterns of coordinating fibers that control the beating. The ciliate is unable to swim properly if these fibers are cut with microsurgical tools. They do not constitute a nervous system, for the animal is little more than a single cell, but serve the same general function. In some ciliates, tufts of cilia are fused together and function as little tapering legs. Protozoans of

Among the thousands of species of single-celled protozoans, only three fundamentally different forms of locomotion have evolved. The ciliates, represented here by *Spirostomum* (*left panel*), propel themselves through the water by means of numerous hairlike organs called *cilia*. Flagellates, such as *Euglena* (*center panel*), have evolved a whiplike organ of locomotion called a *flagellum*. The flagellum functions as a sort of one-bladed propeller, with its looping undulations pulling the animal through the water in a characteristic spiral path. The third type of protozoan locomotion is exemplified by *Amoeba* (*right panel*), which moves by means of pseudopodia—literally "false feet." A pseudopodium is an extension of the animal's body, made possible because the cytoplasm, or cell contents, can exist in either of two states, one fluid and one jellylike.

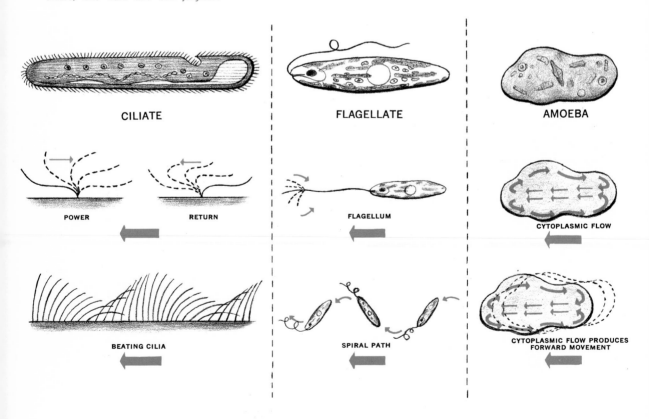

| CILIATE | FLAGELLATE | AMOEBA |

POWER   RETURN   FLAGELLUM   CYTOPLASMIC FLOW

BEATING CILIA   SPIRAL PATH   CYTOPLASMIC FLOW PRODUCES FORWARD MOVEMENT

this type resemble scurrying mice as they creep through detritus in the field of a microscope.

Although the familiar *Amoeba* does not swim, some kinds of *Amoeba* can remain suspended in the water by forming long ray-shaped extensions of cytoplasm. A few related species that are frequently picked up in plankton tows, the "sun animals," or heliozoans, have raylike extensions of exceptional beauty.

Take a breath

Nearly all living cells require oxygen in order to release the energy locked in food. The complicated process by which cells methodically break down and release energy from food is known as *cellular respiration.* It is not the same process as breathing, which we call "respiration." Breathing is simply the act of acquiring oxygen from the air by means of a functional device such as a lung. As we have seen, pond plants may store some of the oxygen of photosynthesis in the airspaces of their stems during the day and then draw upon these reserves at night. Pond animals, on the other hand, do not produce any oxygen of their own, but they have developed some unusual ways of obtaining it.

Many creatures—turtles, frogs, immature and adult insects, and some snails—live more or less permanently in a pond but breathe atmospheric oxygen. Frogs have slightly elevated nostrils, and some turtles have elongated noses that poke out through the surface without any other part of the head showing. Snorkels of this sort allow an animal to remain submerged while it replenishes its air supply.

More extreme examples are found among insects. The water scorpion has a pair of posterior filaments which, when pressed together, form a breathing tube. Rat-tailed maggots, larval insects found in low-oxygen waters along pond margins, have telescopic breathing tubes of remarkable proportions; when fully extended, they can be four times the length of the insect's body. Mosquito larvae wriggle upward through the water to the surface, where they poke a small snorkel through the elastic film. The tip of this tube is equipped with tiny hairs that repel water and thus keep the tube open to the air for as long as the larva hangs there. Mosquito pupae have a pair of similar tubes that open from the enlarged midregion of the body, rather than from the tip of the abdomen as in the larvae.

How beetles breathe

When you sit by a pond and watch the activity of large aquatic insects, you will be impressed by the frequency with which many of these active creatures come to the surface. They dart up, hang head downward from the film for a few seconds, and then swim down and out of sight. Like all adult insects, each of these creatures has throughout its body a network of very fine tubules, the tracheal system. Air passes in and out of this system through a series of pores, or *spiracles*. The actual exchange of air is brought about by the expansion and contraction of the abdomen, rather like the action of bellows.

The spiracles of aquatic insects open either to a reserve of trapped air carried outside the insect's body or to the rear of the abdomen. *Dytiscus* is a good example of an insect that carries an air supply down with it. Its large, heavy wing covers shield air bubbles trapped underneath them. The insect draws upon this air as needed, but periodically it has to return to the surface to replenish the supply.

If you look at other adult insects underwater, or in an aquarium, you are sure to notice that they, too, carry air in some fashion—under wing covers, on the underside of the body, or perhaps encasing the entire body. While some may use the air directly, as large diving beetles do, others make use of it in a different way.

Physical gills

Land animals that have returned to an aquatic environment have not changed their lungs back to gills. Whales, sea lions, otters, turtles, and other aquatic mammals and reptiles all have to surface to breathe. It might be to their advantage if they could extract oxygen from water, but none of them can. One animal group now living in water but originally from the land—aquatic insects—has partially solved this problem.

Backswimmers, certain other diving bugs, and small diving beetles carry air bubbles underwater. These bubbles act as "physical gills" rather than as biological, or living, gills.

A backswimmer uses up the original oxygen supply, contained in the bubble, in a few minutes, yet it remains submerged and active for much longer periods of time. How?

The half-inch whirligig beetle is primarily an inhabitant of the surface film, but it occasionally dives, with a bubble of air trapped beneath its wing covers and partially protruding near the tip of its abdomen. At the surface the beetle obtains oxygen directly from the atmosphere, but when it is submerged the air bubble acts as a physical gill. As a larva the insect possesses true fleshy gills which extract oxygen from the water.

Oxygen from the surrounding water continually diffuses through the surface film of the bubble and maintains its contents at the normal atmospheric ratio of twenty percent oxygen and eighty percent nitrogen. A diving insect gets rid of carbon dioxide in just the reverse fashion: the insect simply exhales it into the bubble, and it readily diffuses into the water.

You might think that their physical gills would allow these small diving insects to remain permanently submerged, but such is not the case. Their bubbles gradually decrease in size as nitrogen escapes slowly into the water. So these insects do have to surface to replenish their bubbles, though much less frequently than the large diving beetles. Some adult insects, however, can stay underwater almost indefinitely. The water boatman, for example, uses the air between its wings and body so efficiently that it seldom comes to the surface. And many of the extremely small aquatic adult insects never come to the surface at all. Their bodies are covered with densely packed water-repellent hairs, two million to a square millimeter. Beneath the

When submerged, the backswimmer breathes by means of a physical gill, a bubble of air through which oxygen is absorbed from the surrounding water and waste carbon dioxide is discharged. Although the backswimmer must eventually return to the surface to renew the bubble, this unusual adaptation allows the insect to remain underwater for as long as six hours.

canopy formed by these tiny hairs there is a layer of air which functions as a highly efficient physical gill. But such an arrangement works well only in shallow water, for the pressure of deeper water compresses the air and makes breathing impossible. Insects with physical gills of this type have organs that sense increasing pressure and help them to stay close to the surface. In fact, all aquatic insects have sensory organs for detecting changes in light and pressure and maintaining their equilibrium. Diving beetles, water boatmen, water scorpions, and backswimmers are well oriented in their three-dimensional world.

Living gills

Immature insects without snorkels or physical gills have several methods of breathing. The nymphs of damselflies, dragonflies, and mayflies and the larvae of caddisflies have tracheal systems that have no spiracles. Dissolved oxygen enters their tracheal systems by diffusing through the thin-walled cuticles surrounding their bodies. Many species have body walls with feathery or flattened extensions that provide increased areas for absorbing oxygen. The tracheal system of the caddisfly larva actually enters branched finger-like gills on the underside of its body.

Most midge larvae do not have well-developed tracheal systems. They obtain oxygen by means of fingerlike gills extending outside their bodies, in which a colorless blood circulates. But midges that live where there is very little oxygen dissolved in the water may have bright red blood containing a pigment closely related to *hemoglobin*, the pigment that colors our own blood. Because oxygen diffuses much more rapidly into blood with hemoglobin than into blood without it, these larvae can get the oxygen they need even in impoverished surroundings.

If you collect a few midge larvae or mayfly nymphs and place them in a container of clear water, you may notice

Certain aquatic insects breathe underwater by means of an air bubble, or physical gill. The bubble acts as a link between the water and the insect's respiratory system, a network of tiny branching tubes which carry oxygen (*green arrows*) to the body tissues and remove carbon dioxide (*black arrows*) from them. As the original oxygen supply in the bubble is used up, more oxygen diffuses in from the surrounding water, and simultaneously carbon dioxide discharged from the insect's tissues diffuses out into the water. The bubble slowly gets smaller as nitrogen escapes into the water, and eventually the insect rises to the surface to take on a fresh supply of air. Water-repellent hairs at the tip of the insect's abdomen help to anchor it in the surface film and prevent water from entering its respiratory system.

The bright red color of "bloodworms" results from the presence of an oxygen-storing substance chemically related to the hemoglobin of human blood. These are not worms at all, but the larvae of a midge somewhat resembling a stingless mosquito. In oxygen-poor water, the larvae set up currents by rhythmically snapping their bodies into an S curve.

127

peculiar rhythmic movements after a while. Deprived of the gentle water currents of the pond, the insects quickly deplete the oxygen reserves in the immediate vicinity. Soon they begin moving their bodies and producing currents that bring fresh supplies of oxygen. Midge larvae wriggle their bodies inside the tubes of detritus that they construct around themselves. Mayfly nymphs wave flat platelike gills attached to the sides of their abdomens. Some of the larger dragonflies pump water in and out of abdominal chambers that have tracheal tubes embedded in their walls.

A few highly specialized insect larvae live in currents created by other organisms. The larvae of the little spongillaflies, *Sisyra*, live on the surface of fresh-water sponges, which they parasitize. In their internal cavities sponges have great numbers of microscopic flagellated cells, which cause water to flow in through many small pores and empty out through a few larger pores. In this way sponges obtain both food and oxygen. *Sisyra* larvae suck cell fluids from sponges with their piercing mouthparts, and they also benefit from the constant flow of water around them. Similarly, certain parasitic water mites, *Unionicola*, inhabit the gill chambers of fresh-water mussels or clams and take advantage of the continual supply of fresh oxygenated water produced by the curtainlike expanse of their bivalve hosts' heavily ciliated gills.

Besides mussels, there are other complex animals in the pond, such as amphipods, isopods, and crayfish, that have well-developed gills. Both amphipods and isopods have small gills that can be seen easily with a magnifying glass. An isopod's gills are toward the rear of its body, arranged like the leaves of a book under a protective cover. They fan rapidly, creating currents of water that bring fresh supplies of oxygen.

How crayfish breathe

The crayfish is a miniature version of the North American sea lobster. Knowing the anatomy of one will suffice for the other, although their habitats are very different indeed. A crayfish's gills are to the sides under the front and middle portions of its body, protected by a strong covering, a part of the exoskeleton. The covering is free along the bottom margin, and through this opening water is drawn into a gill

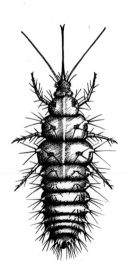

Shortly after hatching, the quarter-inch larva of the spongillafly takes up residence on a fresh-water sponge, its body bristles serving both as holdfasts and as camouflage. The water currents that are set up by the sponge bathe the larva in oxygen-rich water, and the host's soft body tissues yield nourishing juices to the larva's sucking mouthparts. Curiously enough, the larva's digestive tract has no posterior opening, so that any undigested or waste material must be retained within its body.

chamber on each side. A current of water is created by two gill bailers, specialized appendages toward the front of the animal, near the mouth, which fan rapidly like small propellers. If you watch a crayfish in a tank, you can see particles in the water being drawn up along the sides of its body and then shot out toward the front with great speed.

You may be able to find a female crayfish carrying her eggs or young attached to her swimmerets, paired appendages under her abdomen. She continually fans the swimmerets, thus assuring her developing young of a constant supply of oxygenated water.

Crayfish can spend considerable time out of water, provided their gills remain wet. Some species, such as the one shown here, burrow in the marshy soil of pond margins. Crayfish excavate their burrows only at night, bringing up pellets of mud and depositing them around the entrances to form "chimneys."

Breathing without gills

Many of the smaller animals that live in ponds have neither gills nor lungs. *Hydra*, copepods, and the planarian flatworm *Dugesia* have one thing in common: none of their cells is very far from the surrounding water. *Hydra* is tubular, with water both inside and out, and has only two layers of cells to its body. The flatworm has many more cells arranged in three layers, but its entire body is very flat and no cells are far from the outside. Copepod crustaceans are rather thick-bodied, but they are so small that oxygen easily diffuses throughout their tissues. The even smaller protozoans, each composed of only one "super cell," have no problem whatsoever.

129

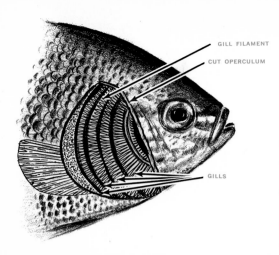

GILL FILAMENT
CUT OPERCULUM
GILLS

Fish, such as the pumpkinseed sunfish pictured below, breathe with gills that are located under a pair of protective covers called *opercula*, just behind the head. Beneath the opercula, the gills are arranged in feathery filaments supported by bony arches, usually four in number. The gill filaments overlap like shingles, with spaces between, through which water can pass. The gill tissue is filled with tiny blood vessels, into which oxygen diffuses from water washing over the gills; waste carbon dioxide is lost from the blood stream simultaneously into the water.

A *fish pump*

When a fish looks at you through the walls of an aquarium, it remains suspended in midwater, silently opening and closing its mouth. To breathe properly, the fish must constantly pass water over its gills. When it opens its mouth, a partial vacuum is formed and water rushes in. If you look closely as the mouth closes again, you will see a pair of flaps, or valves, coming together just inside the mouth. Once these oral valves and the mouth are closed, the water that the fish has "swallowed" can escape only through the gill slits on the sides of its head.

Each gill consists of a series of Y-shaped filaments containing arteries that are separated from the water by a layer of tissue only one cell thick. Because blood coming to the gills is deficient in oxygen, there is a natural tendency for oxygen in the water to diffuse into the fish's blood stream. Since blood is coursing rapidly through the gills and water is being constantly pumped past them, the oxygenation of the fish's blood is rapid and very effective.

Normally the movements of a fish's mouth and gill covers occur at a moderate pace, but they accelerate greatly when the water becomes too warm, or whenever the oxygen level drops below normal. In winter, however, when the water is very cold, a fish's breathing movements slow down markedly.

Of all the pond's inhabitants, fish have by far the most complex, and at the same time the most adaptable, system for obtaining dissolved oxygen.

To breathe, a fish must maintain a constant flow of water over its gills by means of a kind of two-cycle pump. On the intake stroke, the opercula are closed and water is drawn through an oral valve by an outward expansion of the "cheeks." On the discharge stroke, the opercula are opened, the oral valve is closed, and the cheeks are contracted, forcing the water outward over the gills. Depending on the species of fish and the temperature and oxygen content of the water, this cycle may occur from twelve times a minute to over one hundred times a minute.

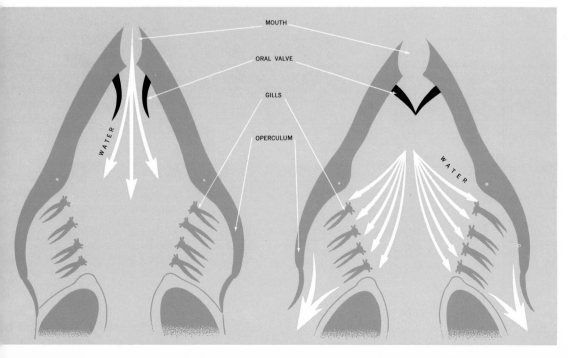

MOUTH

ORAL VALVE

GILLS

OPERCULUM

WATER

WATER

Diving birds

If fish are superbly adapted to life in water, they are utterly unsuited to life anywhere else. Some of the pond's inhabitants, however, have the best of two worlds: they are air breathers, and yet special respiratory adaptations allow them to be excellent underwater swimmers as well. These versatile animals are the diving birds—grebes, loons, mergansers—which spend much of their time gathering food below the pond's surface. Aquatic birds have extensions of their lungs throughout their bodies which make them buoyant when they swim. When they are preparing to dive, they exhale much of the air in their lungs and air sacs, thus making it easier to submerge. They still have enough oxygen to stay under a long time, because their blood is exceptionally rich in hemoglobin and holds more oxygen than the blood of most other birds. Also, when they dive, their

Rising out of the depths like a surfacing submarine, this pied-billed grebe may be returning from a dive to the bottom of the pond, where it pursues fish and other small animals.

heartbeat slows down, as does their general metabolism, and only their brains, sensory organs, and muscles receive their normal quotas of oxygen. Carbon dioxide accumulates in their systems but is exhaled when the birds reach the surface.

A hungry multitude

Getting enough oxygen is a solution to only one of life's problems. Every organism must eat as well as breathe. Probably civilized man is the only creature on earth who can eat in a leisurely fashion. Almost every other creature, no matter where it lives, must either constantly feed itself or constantly be on the lookout for food.

Primary consumers among the zooplankton are very small, but they have high metabolic rates and expend energy rapidly. They must graze continuously in the floating pastures of diatoms, desmids, and flagellates. Copepods have special filter "mills," formed by their legs and other appendages, with which they rake in quantities of microscopic plants.

Clumsy on land, awkward even in the air, the grebe is in its true element in the water, where it swims and dives with superb skill. A variety of body adaptations allow the bird to remain underwater for an exceptionally long time before it must return to the surface for air.

133

Heads down and tails up, dabbling green-winged teals find a variety of foodstuffs in the shallows of a pond. Water plants make up ninety percent of their diet; insects, mollusks, and fish account for the rest.

A tadpole spends nearly all of its time scraping off algal coatings from plant stems, stones, and the bottom with its horny, rasping beak. Many young fish, when they first hatch from eggs, feed indiscriminately upon all plankton. Since they hatch in the spring, when phytoplankton blooms, they consume mostly floating algae of various sorts.

The littoral vegetation usually is not nearly so important a food source as the phytoplankton, but many creatures do depend upon it. Underwater, map turtles and painted turtles eat some of the more tender plants, such as waterweed, that grow from the bottom. Fish eat waterweed as well as fanwort, hornwort, and widgeon grass, to name only a few others. Ducks and geese eat many of the submerged plants, including pondweeds, widgeon grass, tape grass, starwort, and water nymph. They also eat floating plants near the shore, such as water shield, white water lilies, and duckweed. Other animals eat the white water lily as well: moose, beavers, muskrats, and porcupines eat the leaves, and snails and insects eat parts of the stem.

Probably the emergent plants nourish more land animals than aquatic animals. You will find a variety of large and small mammals, birds, turtles, insects, and snails feeding in the dense stands of emergent plants that fringe a pond.

Ponds in Canada and the northern United States may be visited by moose, such as this cow and her calf, which feed on spatterdock, white water lilies, and other aquatic plants. The animals select favorite ponds and visit them repeatedly, usually in the early morning or the evening.

134

Deer, such as this white-tailed doe, are frequent visitors to ponds, not only to drink and to browse on spatterdock and other vegetation, but apparently also to enjoy a dip in the water. The best time to see these shy animals is early in the morning or just after sunset.

The catchers and the eaten

As you drift quietly in a boat across a pond, you may hear a rapid series of high, cheeping whistles far overhead. Looking up, you see a great brown and white hawk circling. It hovers, folds its wings, and dives straight down into a patch of yellow water lilies. It hits with a loud splash, throwing water into the air, and disappears for a moment. Then, shedding drops in a glistening spray and rising into the air with powerful beats of its great wings, the hawk—an osprey —reappears, clutching a bass in its talons. It flies directly to a dead tree overhanging the edge of the pond, shifts the fish about with its claws, and pecks at it. Then the bird takes off and flies out of sight, still holding the fish tightly. To watch the hunting of an osprey is a thrilling experience, and one you will not forget, for it is likely to be the most dramatic example of predation you will see in a pond.

Other hunters are not so easy to see. From a distance you may glimpse a rippling wake in the water and then a sudden churning turmoil. A few moments later a sleek otter emerges on the shore nearby and bounds away with a large glistening fish in its mouth. Later, as you sit rocking gently in your boat, you are alarmed by a thunderous snap and splash in the nearby lily pads. The water swirls, then quiets down, and all is as before. What was it? Probably a large snapping turtle crept along the bottom up to a basking frog or fish and then, with lightning speed, thrust out its long neck and clamped down its sharp jaws on the victim.

There is something rather impressive about a turtle weighing thirty, forty, or even as much as sixty or seventy pounds, but a pond usually cannot support more than a very few such giants. Snapping turtles occupy the peak in a pyramid of numbers and have a fairly limited food supply. Although they may occasionally drag ducks beneath the surface, waterfowl certainly do not commonly figure in their diets. They eat more plant material than anything else, followed by fish, dead organisms, and invertebrates.

The pond offers no more thrilling sight than that of an osprey hovering fifty feet above the surface, then plummeting talons-first into the water and coming up with a fat wriggling fish. Occasionally an osprey, strictly a fish eater, will drown through locking its talons into prey too large to lift from the water.

Large snappers are formidable creatures on land, and will lunge out at hands and feet that come too close. Underwater, however, they appear to have only one thought in mind when they see a boat or a human swimmer, and that is to get away. They strike out at food underwater, but not at things that merely irritate them. While they are hardly the sort of creatures that make good pets, they are much maligned and too often overhunted.

On a sunny day as you walk along the shore, you may see a brightly banded snake slip from a log into the water. Despite the fact that water moccasins live in the Deep South, far from this pond in the Middle Atlantic states, you might think that you have seen one and give the region a wide berth. What you have actually seen is a water snake, which lives around streams and ponds. It is very timid and, along with its near relative the queen snake, is seldom seen even though it is common. Catching one is a touchy business, for water snakes are very pugnacious and make every attempt to bite, but their bite is not at all poisonous.

Water snakes feed almost entirely on frogs, toads, salamanders, and fish, although occasionally they will catch crayfish, shrews, and mice. The smaller queen snakes are much more selective and eat almost nothing but crayfish. Only rarely will they catch frogs or fish. These handsome

Out of water, a full-grown snapping turtle is a formidable antagonist with sharp, strong jaws. Hunters and fishermen exaggerate the extent to which the omnivorous snapper preys on waterfowl and game fish; detailed studies have shown that the bulk of the big turtle's diet comprises aquatic plants, carrion, and various invertebrates.

snakes are at times abundant in ponds with thick vegetation around their shorelines and with large crayfish populations.

The bullfrog

On a summer night a familiar sound along the shores of a pond is the *jug-o'-rum, jug-o'-rum* of a male bullfrog, the largest of the North American frogs. When a male bullfrog calls, it keeps its mouth and nostrils closed and drives air back and forth between its lungs and mouth. The tones created are amplified by the swelling floor of its mouth, which forms a kind of sound chamber. Both male and female bullfrogs are capable of another sound, one that can frighten you half out of your wits. If the frog is grasped around the hind legs and picked up, or perhaps captured by a heron or snapping turtle, it may emit a piercing, terrifying scream which is probably caused by air rushing out of its lungs and

Harmless to humans but the nemesis of frogs, crayfish, and other small pond animals, this banded water snake is one of about a dozen native species of the genus *Natrix*. Like the snapping turtle, the water snake is sometimes accused of decimating game fish; the opposite is true, however, for the snake improves fish populations by culling out diseased and crippled individuals.

141

A four-inch minnow, slowed by injury or disease, is seized and stilled by an eighteen-inch northern water snake. Once the prey has stopped its convulsive flopping, the snake proceeds to swallow it headfirst, a little at a time—in this instance, the process occupied about four minutes in all. The water snake's teeth, while nonvenomous, are sizable and can deliver mortal wounds to the small animals on which the reptile feeds.

THE FISHERMAN'S BEST FRIEND

Fishermen look upon the water snake as an unwelcome competitor for the pond's game fish. Far from being a competitor, however, the water snake is a valuable ally to the fisherman, for in ponds where the snakes are active, the game-fish population tends toward large and vigorous specimens. By preying on minnows, chub, and other small, slow-moving fishes, the snakes hold in check species that compete for food with the bass and pickerel that interest the fisherman. Such game fish that do fall prey to the snakes are almost invariably diseased, injured, or deformed, and the elimination of such individuals helps improve the quality of the overall pond population.

Because the bones of
their jaws and skulls are
joined by stretchable
ligaments, snakes are able
to swallow seemingly
impossibly large prey,
such as this bullfrog
being consumed by a
water snake. The snake's
backward-pointing teeth
assist in this process but
are not used for chewing;
the prey goes down
whole and is dissolved
by the snake's powerful
digestive fluids.

The largest of American frogs, a full-grown bullfrog may have an eight-inch body and ten-inch hind legs. Anything that moves and is not too large to be stuffed into the bullfrog's ample mouth is fair game: insects like the dragonfly being eaten here, smaller frogs, whole crayfish, and even small birds and mammals. Bullfrogs have been known to live for fifteen years.

up its windpipe. Once you hear the scream, you will never forget it, especially if you hear it out by a pond on a dark night.

Bullfrogs are solitary animals and are more aquatic than most frogs, spending nearly all their time floating in the water and diving to the bottom. They do not inhabit every portion of a pond's shore, but seek areas overgrown with willows and other shrubs, where roots and stems form tangled mats.

Bullfrogs are not discriminating eaters. They reach with their muscular, elongated tongues for a variety of creatures —insects, small frogs, young snakes, small fish, indeed almost anything that moves and will fit into their mouths.

144

Underwater hunters

When you enter a bed of yellow water lilies or other plants with flexible emergent stems, sit quietly and wait for action. It may not be long in coming. Not far away the stems will begin to move suddenly as a fleeing fish brushes against them, taking the most direct route of escape. The passage of the fish is marked clearly by the moving, bending plants. Close behind comes a mighty rush, and the plants dance and sway as a larger and far more powerful creature surges through the water. You can only guess, but judging from the speed it displays, you decide that it must be an attacking pickerel. Although not related to the barracuda, the pickerel is similar in many ways to this great marine predator. Both hang motionless for long periods of time; both patrol definite regions; both are elongated and arrow-straight; both attack by sight with blinding speed; and both have sharply pointed teeth. A favorite pickerel locale is among emergent vegetation, especially in the deep shadows under lily pads.

Pickerels do not tolerate competition, and so where one is found, others will not be near. The larger pickerels have territories which they police, and in which they do most of their feeding. Anything that comes their way is fair prey; they will capture and devour ducklings, frogs, fish, small snakes, newly hatched turtles, insects, and crayfish.

Chain pickerel, grass (mud) pickerel, and redfin pickerel are the species common in ponds. Although far smaller than their relatives, the lake-dwelling northern pike or the great muskellunge, they are no less ferocious.

A streamlined pickerel watching for prey often hovers motionless just below the pond's surface, its dappled markings blending with the shadows of floating vegetation. The victim, seized in a lightning-fast forward rush and swallowed whole, is most frequently another fish, but any creature large enough to attract the pickerel's attention may fall prey to it.

Insect predators

Among the pond's most ferocious insect predators are the giant water bugs, of which there are a number of species, some over three inches in length. Giant water bugs grasp their prey—fish, frogs, tadpoles, other insects—with their powerful forelegs, paralyze them with injections of poison, and suck out their body juices.

A large diving beetle is a good example of the highly successful hunter, as is the equally large giant water bug. The latter is predacious and captures insects, tadpoles, fish, and even small frogs with its large, jackknife front legs. Once it holds its victim in its powerful grasp, the giant water bug injects a paralytic poison through its beak. If you pick one up, do so carefully, for the bug can give you a very painful bite.

The nymphs of the large dragonflies are among the most impressive underwater predators. Nymphs differ according to the kind of habitat in which they live. Stream and brook dragonfly nymphs are constructed quite differently from those of still waters. Depending on the species, a pond nymph may burrow into the mud, sprawl on top of the soft bottom, or cling to plant stems above the bottom. Most of these forms hunt primarily by sight, although some of the sprawlers depend more on touch.

Should you catch a large dragonfly nymph, place it in a container of pond water. If fed regularly on small worms or midge larvae, it should live successfully through the winter. It is well worth watching, for its feeding technique is amazing. The so-called underlip, or *labium,* of a dragonfly nymph consists of a long folded structure, hinged both where it joins the body and in the middle. At the tip is a pair of overlapping jaws.

Some nymphs stalk their prey, and others lie in wait. No matter which is the case, a sudden increase in blood pressure causes a lightning-fast extension of the labium when a victim comes within reach. The entire labium may extend an inch beyond the head of a very large nymph. The jaws at the tip of the labium, which are under the control of the nervous system, close on whatever they strike. The prey, usually another insect, a worm, or a crustacean, is then brought back to the mouth when a decrease in blood pressure allows the labium to fold under the head. While the true jaws and mouthparts of a nymph crush the food, the labium continues to hold it firmly in position. Further chewing goes on in a gizzard within the body of the insect.

If you keep nymphs in a shallow container of water and feed them enough, you should be prepared for the outcome of such feasting—a large nymph can expel a pellet of waste material at least a foot out of water.

146

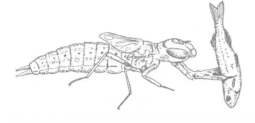

Alert and able to strike with lightning speed, the dragonfly nymph is one of the pond's dominant insect carnivores. It preys on anything smaller than itself— other insects, crustaceans, snails, worms, and small fish. The nymph captures its prey with a specially adapted lower lip called a labium. Normally folded back under the head, the labium shoots far out to grasp the victim and drag it back to the mouth and jaws.

On a far smaller scale, other insect predators can be found in the pond. Among the zooplankton there are the phantom midge larva *Chaoborus* and a bizarre water flea, *Leptodora*. Both rise close to the surface at night and capture copepods, common water fleas, small larval insects, worms, and other planktonic drifters. Both are elongated, very active, and transparent.

The elongated *Leptodora*, largest of all fresh-water cladocerans, may reach three-quarters of an inch in length. An active predator, *Leptodora* darts vigorously through the water in pursuit of small worms, insects, and other members of the pond's zooplankton.

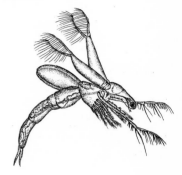

An eight-eyed wonder

If there is a dock reaching out into your pond, look underneath. Certainly there will be many kinds of spiders present, some of which spin webs that trap the multitudes of midges and other flying insects that emerge from the water. On a piling near the water you may find one of the large fisher spiders, possibly a specimen with a leg spread of several inches. It makes no webbed trap but spins only a life line, a few strands that slow its descent should it fall. It is an active, capable predator that captures insects and even tadpoles and small fish. At night you can find fisher spiders with ease, for their eyes reflect a flashlight's beam with eight cold, green pinpoints of light.

The fisher spider, *Dolomedes,* is a handsome creature, plentifully endowed with hairlike extensions of its outer skeleton. The hair serves several functions: its color often resembles the background on which the fisher spider rests; each hair has a sensory function, and the spider responds if one is touched; and the hair increases the surface area of the spider. The last function is an important one. Fisher spiders often skate across the pond surface at night: they are among the largest of all animals to be supported by the surface film. The thousands of hairs distribute the fisher spider's weight evenly over a large area, causing the surface film to be depressed, but not to break. Then, if the spider goes underwater by pulling itself beneath a floating leaf or down a piling, the highly water-repellent hairs trap a complete coating of air, which gives the animal enough oxygen to breathe for at least three-quarters of an hour.

Although fisher spiders most frequently prey on insects, a tadpole or small fish sometimes falls victim to its venomous jaws. Relying entirely on its hunting skill to capture food, the fisher spider spins a net only as a nursery for its young, which number about three hundred.

149

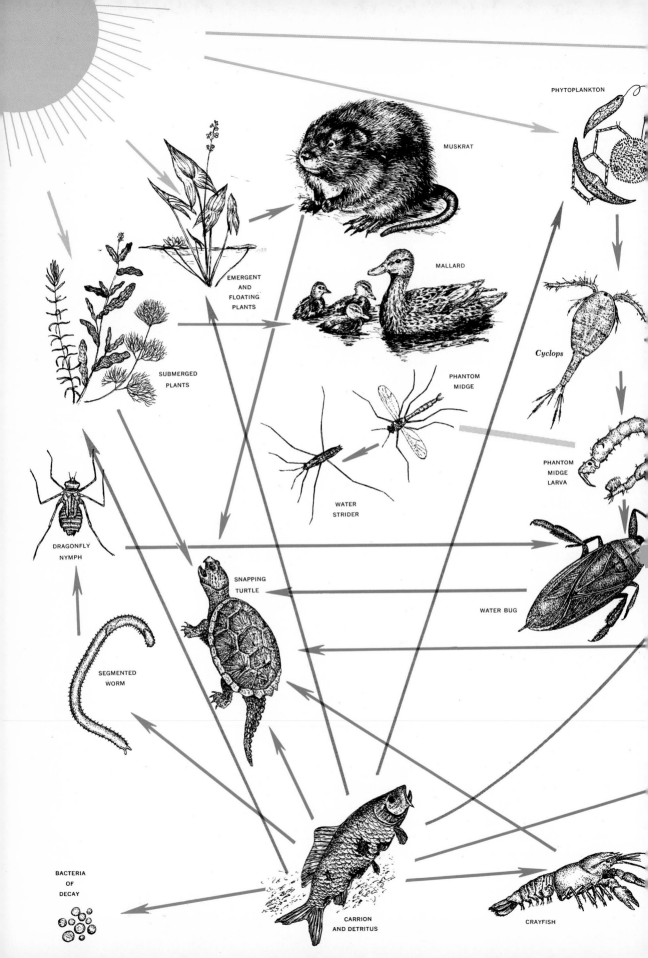

PHYTOPLANKTON

MUSKRAT

MALLARD

EMERGENT
AND
FLOATING
PLANTS

Cyclops

PHANTOM
MIDGE

SUBMERGED
PLANTS

PHANTOM
MIDGE
LARVA

WATER
STRIDER

DRAGONFLY
NYMPH

SNAPPING
TURTLE

WATER BUG

SEGMENTED
WORM

BACTERIA
OF
DECAY

CARRION
AND DETRITUS

CRAYFISH

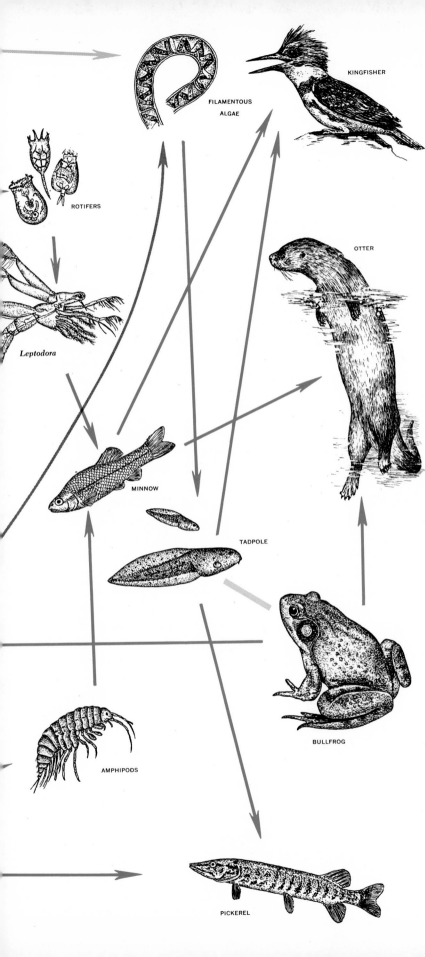

FILAMENTOUS ALGAE

KINGFISHER

ROTIFERS

Leptodora

OTTER

MINNOW

TADPOLE

AMPHIPODS

BULLFROG

PICKEREL

THE POND'S WEB OF ENERGY

Shown here is a *food web*, a means of representing the complex set of energy relationships binding together the members of a natural community. The arrows represent the direction of flow of energy; that is, they point from the consumed to the consumer. Orange arrows represent solar energy; gray arrows, simple nutrient substances; dark green arrows, the main flow of food energy; light green bars, growth and development. Though the diagram is necessarily highly simplified and illustrates only a fraction of the interdependencies that operate in the pond, the fundamental features of food-energy transfer are readily apparent. The sun is the ultimate source of energy. Its light powers a series of chemical reactions within the pond's green plants. Carbon dioxide from the air is combined with hydrogen from water molecules to produce the basic foodstuffs upon which the entire community is dependent. The importance of the phytoplankton is evident in this diagram: trace back through the food chains of the big predators like the otter and pickerel, and you will see that even they are ultimately dependent on these tiny drifting plants. The crayfish illustrates still another basic ecological function: as a scavenger it converts minute bits of detritus, useless as such to animals like the pickerel and snapping turtle, into crayfish protoplasm, which these larger organisms may eat. Finally, the diagram points out the intricate nature of any natural community, and shows why human interference with any single link in its food web can have far-reaching and often unpredictable effects throughout that community.

To live with another

Two animals may be associated in a number of ways besides the eater-and-eaten relationship of predation. *Trichodina*, a specialized protozoan living on *Hydra* tentacles (*top*), illustrates *commensalism*, in which one or both animals benefit from the relationship, although neither is entirely dependent upon it. *Phoresis* is an even looser relationship, a more or less accidental association, as in the case of these peritrichs attached to a copepod (*bottom*).

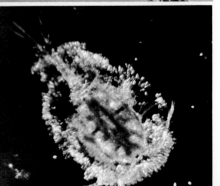

Predation is only one way of life. There are other basic types of relationships existing between animals, and many examples of intimate or *symbiotic* associations can be found among common pond organisms.

First, there is *phoresis*, a kind of accidental relationship that is not necessary for either of the two partners. Certain pond protozoans, the peritrichs, are stalked and attach to fixed objects, usually to bits of submerged detritus or plant stems. Occasionally, one will attach to a living animal. An animal's body may be an even better place to attach than a fixed object, since the host animal will move about and thereby carry the peritrichs to fresh supplies of oxygen and food, which they filter from the water. Peritrichs may fasten to the shells of turtles, to crustaceans, or to slower-moving insects. You may find them on the cases of caddisfly larvae. Sometimes a copepod will have so many peritrichs on it that they will inhibit its movements and perhaps even cause its death.

Another example of phoresis in ponds involves the freshwater sponges. Their shapes vary from broad carpets to tall fingerlike projections, very irregular and with many internal spaces. Inside a sponge live a variety of animals, including flatworms, immature and adult insects, rotifers, crustaceans, segmented worms, water mites, roundworms, and snails. All these animals greatly benefit from living in the highly favorable habitat created by the sponge.

A second state of convenience existing between two kinds of organisms is *commensalism*. Usually at least one of the partners benefits to some degree from this relationship. *Trichodina*, a highly specialized peritrich, lives only on the tentacles of *Hydra*, where it can be found scurrying about like a little spool-shaped mouse. If you observe the partnership under a microscope, you will notice that *Trichodina* appears to glide directly over the triggerlike projections that shoot off the *Hydra*'s stinging cells, yet the cells do not explode. *Trichodina* must benefit from food caught and paralyzed by the *Hydra* and probably in turn keeps the surfaces of the tentacles free of silt.

A third relationship, *mutualism*, is a state of true mutual dependency in which each partner has lost its means of independence. There are several examples of this relationship to be found among pond organisms. Two ciliate protozoans, a species of *Stentor* and a species of *Paramecium*, are bright green as a result of being packed with hundreds of very tiny one-celled algae. The algal cells produce simple foodstuffs and oxygen; the animal cells require both and in turn give off carbon dioxide, which the plants need. Both protozoans remain in shallow water, where sunlight is intense. In this species of *Paramecium*, the algae appear to act as light receptors which somehow cause the whole animal to react to light.

A species of green *Hydra* also has algae in its cells. Apparently this *Hydra* initially becomes infected with algae after eating copepods and water fleas with undigested algal cells in their intestines. The fresh-water sponge *Spongilla* at times is bright green from the algae packed within its cells. Unlike the protozoans and the green *Hydra*, however, *Spongilla* is also found without algae, and probably the relationship is not an essential one for the sponge.

Parasites

Finally, there is *parasitism*, a relationship that is not always easy to define. You will recall that ordinary consumers use approximately sixty percent of their food for general metabolism, ten percent for growth and repair, and about three percent for reproduction. A parasite, on the other hand, usually directs less than one percent to general metabolism and less than one percent to growth, but about seventy percent to reproduction. Why? The chances of survival for most of its eggs and young are exceedingly slight. However, if they do reach their chosen host, they are reasonably secure and receive plenty of food.

Almost every animal in the world is parasitized. (We too are well parasitized, whether we like the idea or not.) Certainly there is no pond animal that is without its parasites. Look at a rotifer under a microscope and you will see inside its excretory bladder a number of tiny wriggling flagellates—microscopic parasites in a microscopic host. We have already mentioned two other parasites: *Sisyra*, an insect larva that parasitizes sponges, and the mites that parasitize fresh-water mussels.

Water boatmen, water scorpions, and water striders may be parasitized by water mites, which cling to their feet or hide under their wings. When the insects migrate, the mites

Another example of commensalism is the relationship between this fresh-water sponge (incidentally serving as a resting place for a damselfly larva) and the algae that live in its cells. The algae benefit by being afforded shelter and a source of carbon dioxide; the sponge benefits by receiving oxygen and foodstuffs resulting from the algae's photosynthesis.

are transported to other ponds, and so they can escape from a drying pond in which they would otherwise die. Because of its unique method of breathing, a dragonfly nymph can become infected with parasitic flatworms. The strong currents of water flowing in and out of its abdominal respiratory chamber may carry in some of the fluke larvae that swim in the pond. Once in the nymph, they burrow through its body wall and migrate to muscle tissue, where they encyst.

Many of a pond's fishes are parasitized. Fishermen know that the yellow perch usually harbors internal roundworms, but so do many other fishes in fresh water. Usually infection occurs when fishes eat copepods or other crustaceans in which the worm passes part of its life cycle. On the outside of a fish there can be various kinds of external parasites, one of which is a parasitic copepod crustacean called a fish louse. It clings to the surface of a fish by means of special suckers on its underside.

Perhaps the most unusual of a fish's parasites is not a worm or a crustacean, but a juvenile clam. Fresh-water mussels, or clams, produce at one time up to three million embryos called *glochidia*. A glochidium has two small shells with sharp jointed spines along the free edges. Glochidia are shed from the parent in small bunches. They rest lightly on the bottom, for their density is nearly that of water, and the slightest disturbance not only sends clouds of glochidia swirling up into the water but also sets them snapping their toothed shells together wildly. If the disturbance is caused by a passing fish, several glochidia may be able to snap onto a fin or a gill filament. Once the spines penetrate the fish's skin, they fold back, locking the larval clam in place. The host's skin reacts to the presence of the glochidium and soon covers it with cells. Now thoroughly protected, the glochidium undergoes a complete transformation, or *metamorphosis*, by constructing an entire new set of organs. It obtains food to do this from the host's cells and from the products of its own disintegration. When its de-

The bright red pinheads swimming busily through the pond or creeping over its bottom are water mites. Under magnification they are revealed as rather droll creatures with conspicuous eyes and with four pairs of legs, which mark them as relatives of the spiders rather than of the insects. A wide variety of animals serve as hosts to the larvae of the mites, including insects like the three-inch water scorpion in the lower picture.

The fresh-water clam passes its larval stage as a fish parasite. The newly released larva, called a glochidium, swims through the water and sinks to the bottom, where it snaps its two-part toothed shell until it fastens onto a suitable host fish. It lives in the host's tissue until it transforms into an adult, then leaves the fish and takes up residence in the mud of the pond's bottom.

EMBRYO

EMBEDDED EMBRYOS

MATURE MUSSEL SETTLED ON POND BOTTOM

Here are two animal relationships in one picture: predation on the part of the damselfly, and parasitism on the part of the red mite larvae clinging to the damselfly's body. The damselfly must share with the mite larvae a portion of the nourishment it derives from the insect prey it is eating.

velopment is over, in perhaps two weeks to a month, the cyst breaks open and a fully formed miniature mussel drops out and takes up a free-living existence on the bottom.

Perhaps the most obvious parasites are the leeches, although some of them behave more like predators. American ponds harbor several different kinds of leeches. Some of them live freely; some attack fish, and others attack snails, frogs, reptiles, and mammals—including man. Should you capture a snapping turtle or a musk turtle, it probably will have a number of small leeches around its eyes and neck. Often these leeches are strikingly colored, for not only does the red blood they have taken in show through, but pigment cells in the skin cause greens, blues, and browns to appear as well. Many leeches need to feed only sporadically, since their extensively branched digestive systems serve as storage tanks for blood they have acquired. Some leeches swim actively; others attach themselves by their hind suckers to pebbles or plant stems and wave their bodies outward in search of passing hosts. Leeches are fascinating animals to study if you can overcome your aversion to their parasitic way of life.

A sanitary service

While we do not like parasites, we usually think even less of carrion eaters and scavengers. Jackals and vultures are far from popular, and maggots in dead flesh horrify us. Yet the role of such animals is vital in a community, for they return to circulation materials that otherwise might be locked up for a long time. The bacteria of decay do the greatest amount of work, but animal scavengers are not far behind.

The amount of organic matter in ponds is enormous. Bacterial decay reduces plant fragments to the microscopic particles known as detritus, a source of food for most small bottom-dwelling animals. Crayfish wade through the light, fluffy plant remains that carpet the bottom, picking out all that is succulent and nourishing. Smaller crustaceans, amphipods and isopods, run and kick their way through the detritus, consuming the smaller particles. Planarian flatworms are quick to find an injured and dying snail, insect, or other animal. They creep over it, extrude a long feeding tube, and begin sucking up whatever body fluids are left. A good way of collecting planarians is to tie a piece of

The planarian flatworm is one of the most abundant of the pond's scavengers. The creature is able to locate its food by means of its extreme sensitivity to chemicals in the water. In the drawing below, the concentric circles represent chemicals diffusing from a food source at the center. When a hungry planarian first detects these chemicals, it wags its head to test the water on either side of its path, then swerves in the direction of greatest stimulation. By periodically repeating this sampling procedure, the worm "zeros in" on its food in a long, curving path.

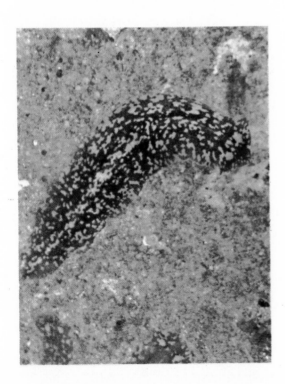

raw liver to a string and lower it to the bottom. When you pull it up later, it should be covered with flatworms if any are present.

Many turtles are active scavengers: snappers, musk turtles, and mud turtles are but a few that eat anything they come across. A great many bottom-dwelling immature insects crawl about, eating either plant detritus or larger plant remains and feeding upon animal carcasses that fall into the water.

All these relationships—phoresis, commensalism, mutualism, parasitism, predation, scavenging—are examples of major *ecological niches*, or ways of life. Every possible ecological niche tends to be occupied in a pond, and once again we are reminded that it truly is a world in miniature. Specializations for swimming, breathing, reproducing, and obtaining food are almost endless, yet they are easily observed by anyone who will take the time to look and to wonder.

These parasitic leeches, attached to the tail fin of a fish, represent one solution to the problems of survival faced by every pond creature. Parasitism is a specialized way of life and is most successful if the parasites do no great harm to the hosts, as is the case here.

Worlds within Worlds

On December 25, 1702, a remarkable Dutchman, Anton van Leeuwenhoek, wrote:

> Whenever I turned my attention to duckweed, I always noticed that it never grows in deep water, even though the water be small and stagnant, and without motion, save such as is imparted to it by the wind; but it is seen in great plenty on broad sheets of water, which are not deep and have little motion, but especially in narrow and shallow ditches. . . .
>
> I got some of the duckweed scooped out of this water in an earthen pot, with lots of water, so that their roots might not be hurt.
>
> I took several of these little weeds out of the pot of water with a needle, one after the other, as nicely as I was able to, and put them in a glass tube of a finger's breadth, that was filled to the top with water, and also in a smaller glass tube, and suffered their little roots to sink down gently; and then examining these roots with the microscope, I beheld with wonder many little animals of divers kinds, which escape our naked eye. . . .

Leeuwenhoek went on to describe several kinds of peritrich protozoans, rotifers, and *Hydra*. He was the first to write

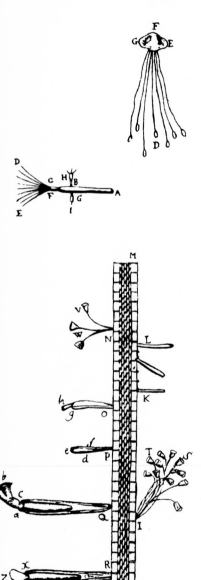

about the fascinating miniature habitat, or *microhabitat*, created by the roots of duckweed.

Life under the duckweed

The microhabitat of a duckweed plant consists of one or more fine filamentous rootlets, less than half an inch long, hanging down under the water's surface film, shaded and protected by the small leaves floating overhead. Here an organism is exposed to plenty of diffused light and plenty of oxygen, but it is not in great danger of being eaten unless a passing duck scoops up the entire duckweed plant.

The plants and animals of the duckweed microhabitat are almost all attaching forms. Desmids, diatoms, and filamentous blue-green algae often are stuck to, or wound around, the roots. A large number of peritrichs, with their bell-shaped ciliated mouths, are always present. Some, such as *Vorticella*, are found singly; some form colonies. Moving up and down the roots are other protozoans of many kinds, which feed on bacteria, algae, and tiny fragments of detritus. Tube-dwelling rotifers and fixed, crowned rotifers extend out from the roots. There are also rotifers that move about. Then there is *Hydra*, the graceful coelenterate with long, drooping tentacles held out in a delicate net to snare passing copepods and water fleas. Predacious insect larvae wriggle from one cluster of roots to another, picking away at the animals attached to the plants. The small leaves overhead and the even tinier watermeal plants may be packed so close together that they form a dry, unbroken canopy on top of which run insects and spiders. Watermeal would not grow so well in some ponds without duckweed, for the larger plants keep the smaller ones from being blown ashore.

So it is evident that where there is duckweed there will also be a host of other plants and animals living close to the surface of the pond. In a cupful of water, you can easily bring home for study a bit of this miniature pond world.

In the miniature jungle of the duckweed community, stalked, bell-shaped **Vorticella** crowd the lower surfaces of the matchhead-sized leaves, and an insect larva thrusts its way between the roots. A **Hydra** (*below*) spreads its sting-laden tentacles among glasslike strands of the alga **Spirogyra**, and funnel-shaped protozoans called **Stentor** swarm through the water.

162

A deathtrap for a home

Bladderwort is another plant that creates a microhabitat for plants and animals. Tangled masses of its stems provide living space for countless fixed, or *sessile*, organisms. Indeed, more sessile rotifers—both numbers of species and numbers of individuals—attach to bladderwort than to any other aquatic plant. On the other hand, waters immediately surrounding bladderwort contain only one-tenth as much plankton as waters farther away. Bladderwort has bladders, or traps, with spines and hairs arranged in definite patterns around their mouths. Small organisms either are caught in the spaces between the hairs or are actually drawn into the traps. A bladder is normally compressed; but when a small creature touches one of its hairs, it suddenly inflates, sucking into its opening whatever is outside. Once inside a bladder, the trapped creature cannot escape, because a transparent valve guards the opening. It dies and is digested and then absorbed by special hairs projecting into the bladder, and so it becomes a part of the plant's food.

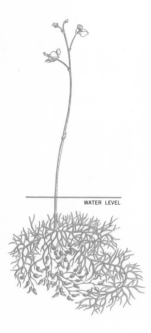

WATER LEVEL

The finely divided leaves of bladderwort (*opposite page*) are studded with rows of deathtrap bladders, each about a tenth of an inch across. The overall plant (*above*) consists of free-floating, branching stems up to three feet long. Aerial stalks bear half-inch flowers which may be blue, yellow, purple, or white, according to species. Each bladderwort bladder is a flattened sac which suddenly expands to suck in any small swimming organism that disturbs the sensitive hairs around its opening. The bladder resets and is ready for more captures in about twenty minutes. The single bladder shown in the close-up (*right*) serves as a base for two tube-dwelling rotifers.

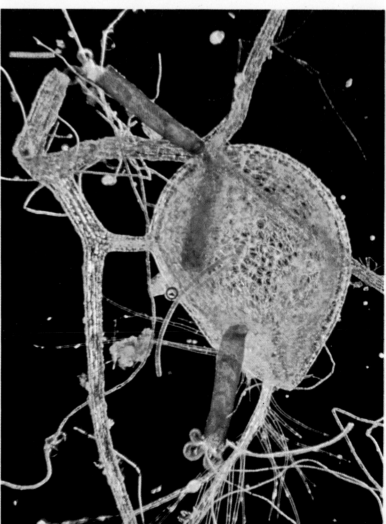

A floating home

A stand of white water lilies forms a world within the world of the pond. The plants' pads provide coves of quiet water in which duckweed and watermeal grow; their water-repellent upper surfaces serve as islands of dry land for insects ranging from dragonflies, like this one at the right of the turtle (*above*), to pinhead-sized jumping plantlice (*below*).

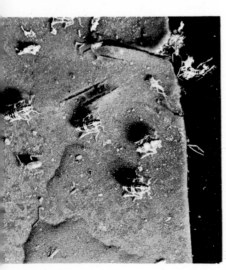

You should not have much difficulty finding a good growth of white pond lily, floating heart, or water shield. A large floating leaf serves as a microhabitat for a surprising number of small animals and plants.

From a few feet away, a lily pad does not seem to be the home of anything more than a few insects. You can see dragonflies and damselflies resting on it briefly and watching for flying prey. As you draw nearer, you may notice a green bug or a ladybird beetle walking about. Perhaps the surface of the leaf is speckled with small white dots; as you reach out to bring the leaf closer, all the dots bound into the air and land on nearby floating leaves or bounce and hop across the surface of the water. You need a magnifying glass to see that they are tiny insects, jumping plantlice and springtails.

A jumping plantlouse uses its legs to leap into the air, but a springtail has a unique apparatus for literally catapulting itself through the air. Two long filaments projecting from the end of the springtail's abdomen are tucked beneath a knob on the underside of its abdomen. When certain muscles contract, the filaments grow tense, but they do not slip off the knob until enough force has been built up for them to snap off violently. When that happens, the springtail shoots off

166

the water surface a foot or more into the air. Upon landing, it automatically rights itself because the knob attracts water.

When you closely examine the upper side of a lily pad, you may see thin discolored channels running through the body of the leaf. These have been cut out by vegetarian insects. One species of aquatic moth caterpillar cuts out two pieces from a lily pad and uses them to make a case in which it lives. But it is not until you turn the leaf over that you realize the full extent of this microhabitat.

Under a lily pad

Dozens of different kinds of animals can live on the slimy, uncluttered undersurfaces of water lily leaves. While no single lily pad will harbor all these creatures together, you will notice several on each leaf if you look closely.

Lily pads afford food as well as lodging to some insect larvae. The pads shown at the left are riddled with irregular channels eaten out by larvae like the one shown above. Although most caterpillars are creatures of the dry land, a few are aquatic, and one of these, the lily-leaf caterpillar, makes itself a protective case by cutting out two circles from a lily pad and lashing them together with strands of silk.

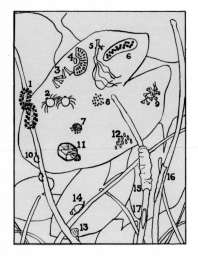

Snails are obvious enough, and three species can usually be found: *Physa*, with a shell like a spiral cone; *Gyraulus*, with a flattened spiral shell resembling a coil of rope; and *Ferrissia*, with its conical shell. Nearby there are likely to be small sausage-shaped masses of jelly with tiny whitish dots within. These dots are snail eggs, and if you look at them through a microscope, you will be able to see the embryonic snails slowly twisting and turning inside.

Tiny water mites scurry over the submerged surface of the water lily leaf, feeding on even smaller creatures. Various species of midge larvae are present, some wandering freely over the underside of the leaf, others encased in small tubes constructed out of detritus and plant fragments. Female damselflies may have attached clusters of eggs to the undersurface, close to the edge. The small round hole in the leaf is the work of a beetle that cuts it out with its jaws, and then inserts its abdomen through the hole and attaches two semicircular rings of eggs to the submerged surface. A young colony of the fresh-water sponge *Spongilla* may be found growing on the leaf or around the lily stem. There may also be a colony of *Cristatella,* one of the few bryozoans, or "moss animals," that are mobile; the whole colony creeps along at a rate of three or four inches a day. Attached to the leaf are rotifers and protozoans of the same species as those on the smaller floating leaves of duckweed. If the white water lily flower has blossomed, it may support a population of thrips, which are among the tiniest of insects.

Living on a stem

Plant stems rising from the bottom support a community of organisms somewhat different from that of the undersurfaces of the leaves. Filamentous green and blue-green algae, desmids, and diatoms thrive on the stems wherever sunlight strikes them. Sponges, bryozoans, and climbing aquatic insects are numerous, and you may even find a small, delicate clam inching its way up with its long, muscular foot.

The insides of stems can also provide a habitat for certain specialized insects and worms that get into either the air-filled or the fluid-filled spaces. Beetle larvae bore into a stem's airspaces to obtain oxygen. Water scorpions, dragonflies, and backswimmers lay their eggs inside air-filled stems, which give the larvae protection and allow them to develop in a high-oxygen environment.

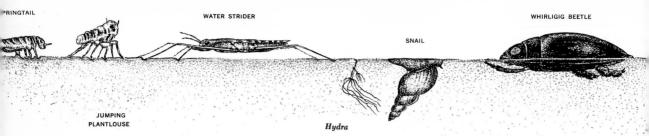

SPRINGTAIL

WATER STRIDER

SNAIL

WHIRLIGIG BEETLE

JUMPING
PLANTLOUSE

Hydra

The surface is a ceiling

Water seems wet enough when you put your hand into it, yet for many organisms it is a firm surface, flexible perhaps, but certainly not fluid. This firmness, a phenomenon known as *surface tension*, results from the strong attraction water molecules have for each other. Beneath the surface, water molecules are attracted to each other from all sides. As a result, the attractive forces acting on one side of a molecule are equalized by forces attracting the opposite side. But at the surface, the molecules are held together only from below and from the sides, since the attraction of water molecules to the air above is slight. The result is a thin but dense layer of water molecules called the *surface film*.

The plants and animals—the neuston—that can make use of the surface film have a large area in which to live, one that stretches across the entire pond. And for those animals not adapted to living on it, the surface film still may be important. An entire group of minnows, known as top feeders,

MOSQUITO LARVA
(breathing position)

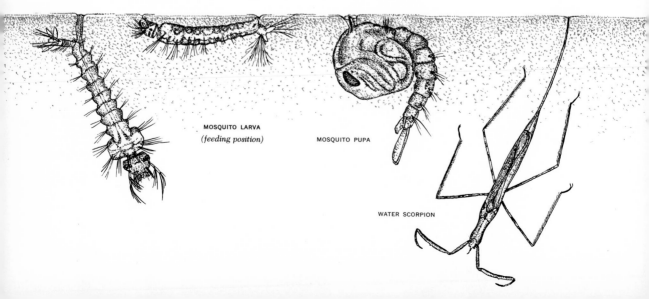

MOSQUITO LARVA
(feeding position)

MOSQUITO PUPA

WATER SCORPION

WATER FLEA

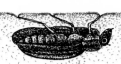

Hydrophilus BEETLE

DUCKWEED   WATERMEAL

ROVE BEETLE

have mouths directed upwards, enabling them to collect food adhering to the film.

In quiet water you may discover a snail crawling along, upside down, under the surface. Close to shore at night, when planarian flatworms come out of hiding, they too may flow smoothly along the undersurface of the film. An occasional *Hydra* may hang down from the film, trailing its tentacles into the water below. Animals that attach themselves to the film in this way can be carried considerable distances by currents, which are caused by friction between water and winds.

A certain water flea is able to hang upside down under the surface because it has a number of waxy hairs that penetrate the film and are held by it. The water flea darts along, rowing itself with feathery antennae, and feeds on submerged algae as well as on pollen blown from land and trapped by the surface film. You may also see a larger animal, a hydrophilid beetle, with water-repellent claws that enable it to walk upside down under the surface film.

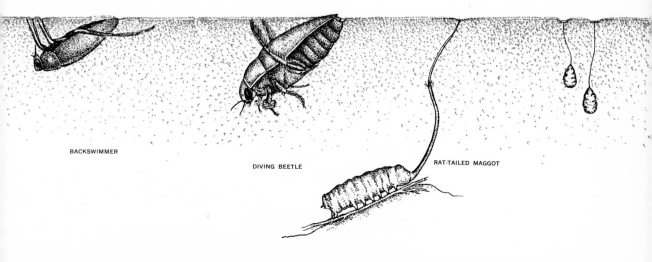

MIDGE EGG MASSES

BACKSWIMMER

DIVING BEETLE   RAT-TAILED MAGGOT

The water strider

Air-breathing creatures that live on top of the surface film, such as the water strider *Gerris* and its smaller relative *Micro-velia*, depend upon its firmness and elasticity just as much as the creatures that live underneath it.

Water striders, or pond skaters, are insects with two pairs of very long legs and one shorter bent pair in front. As you watch one from the shore or from a boat, you will notice that it dimples the water. If the water is shallow, the dimples act as tiny lenses and cast peculiar enlarged shadows with bright margins on the bottom.

A water strider skates across the pond surface by means of the rowing strokes of both its middle and hind legs. The middle legs beat together and appear to be the most effective oars. The "feet," or jointed ends of this insect's legs, have many short waxy hairs and specially arranged claws that repel the water instead of piercing the surface. It is also

possible that the water strider may be able to propel itself by altering the surface tension, but little is known about this at present.

A water strider darts toward moving objects on the surface primarily because it senses light reflections caused by the unevenness of the surface film around the object. If the water strider is a male and the object it sees is a female of the same species, mating may occur. If it turns out to be another male, it is chased away. If it is a dead or dying insect, it is immediately picked up and the body fluids are drained.

A word of caution about collecting water striders: though they live quite well in shallow dishes of water at home, they must not be transported in a jar that contains water. When you carry a jar, water splashes about and soon submerges the insect. Skillful as they are on the surface, water striders drown under the surface film, for they are unable to get back through it to the surface.

The water strider's ability to skim across the water has earned it the name "pond skater" in some areas. Water striders locate their prey in a curious way. They are attracted to any source of bright light and move rapidly toward it. Often the attracting light turns out to be the reflections off the ripples set up by an insect trapped on the surface, and it is on such creatures that the water striders feed.

Insect speedboats

The whirligig beetles of the surface dart in dizzying circles so rapidly that it is almost impossible to follow the course of a single individual. Their paddlelike hind legs, fringed with blades, hang down into the water when they float at rest on the surface film. The upper and lower surfaces of these beetles have distinctly different properties: the upper surface strongly repels water, while the lower does not. As a result the beetles float at a midline, with their backs dry.

Whirligigs are aware of what goes on above and below them simultaneously, by means of very unusual eyes. Most insect eyes are two large hemispheres composed of a great many smaller fixed-focus eyes. The whirligig's eyes are divided into four separate hemispheres, two on each side of the head. The pair of eyes on top look upward into the air; those underneath are directed downward into the water.

The whirligig beetle represents yet another adaptation to life on the surface film. Only the upper surface of the insect is water-repellent, so that it swims half above and half below the surface. As a further adaptation to this way of life, the insect's eyes are divided into two separate pairs—one above the water and one below. This best-of-both-worlds vision must be a strong asset both in locating prey and in avoiding predators.

Like their water strider companions on the surface film, whirligig beetles feed mainly upon the multitude of small animals that fall into the water and are trapped by the same surface film that constitutes a microhabitat for others.

This surface film can be dangerous to animals associated with it, as illustrated by the occasional water strider that is trapped underneath. Then, too, certain creatures may find themselves stranded on top. Water fleas, or cladocerans, are common and abundant members of the zooplankton and usually can be found very close to the surface, where they feed upon diatoms and green algae. If there is any disturbance of the water—a wave, or a ripple caused by a passing boat—some of these tiny animals are thrust up into the air and fall onto the surface. There they remain, quite unable to get themselves back through the tough film, except in one way: they can shed their outer skin by molting and then slip back into the water, leaving the old empty skin floating at the surface.

Breaking through the barrier

For small animals the surface film is a barrier between two different worlds, but it is penetrated regularly by species that must pass from air to water or from water to air in order to mature or to reproduce. Many insects have specialized adaptations that enable them to make the difficult passage. When certain species of damselflies mate, the male grasps the female just behind her head with special claspers at the tip of his abdomen. To begin egg laying, the two alight on the stem of an emergent plant and back down to the water. The female actually submerges and deposits her eggs on the stem well under the surface. When this is done, the male, who is only partly through the film, pulls upward and attempts to fly. The female soon bursts through the surface, and both fly off to repeat the process elsewhere.

Females of some kinds of dragonflies lay eggs one at a time by flying low over the water and flicking the tips of their abdomens down, barely touching the water. This habit gave rise to the older common name for these insects, "darning needles." The speed with which the insects fly keeps them from being caught by surface tension and pulled down.

Our common mosquitoes produce a floating raft of tightly

WATER LEVEL

Mating damselflies fly in tandem (*below*), the male firmly grasping the female just behind her head. Periodically the pair will alight on an emergent plant stem and back down it until the female is partially or totally submerged (*above*). She then inserts single fertilized eggs into the plant tissue.

packed eggs that drift over the surface. The minute larvae hatch through an opening in the bottom of the eggs and emerge directly into the water. Certain midges anchor submerged egg masses with filaments attached to water-repellent disks that float at the surface. Hanging underneath their buoys, the eggs are carried about by winds and water currents. Females of other midges belonging to the same family fly over the water and swish the tips of their abdomens in the water as eggs are released.

The depths of the pond

In the deepest portions of the ocean there are living things unlike any seen around the seashore. Though ponds are not very deep, a somewhat similar situation exists in their benthic, or bottom, regions. This situation is due partly to a lack of light. If a pond is productive, there is so much phytoplankton and zooplankton suspended in the water that only a small amount of light reaches the bottom. This means

Dragonflies also engage in mating flights with the female clasped behind the head by the male. Here, the pair has alighted for a moment, and the female (on the left), to fertilize her eggs, has brought the tip of her abdomen around to a special pocket beneath the male's abdomen in which he has previously stored capsules of sperm. Unlike damselflies, many species of dragonflies simply scatter their eggs at random in the water.

177

that on the bottom very little photosynthesis goes on, and as a result the oxygen content of the water is low. Even so, animals living there have some advantages. Because of the dim light a vulnerable bottom dweller cannot be seen easily, and it has every opportunity to burrow and hide. It does not have to use much energy in moving about; it can spend most of its time resting quietly or walking slowly. Food is plentiful: the bottom is rich in fine detritus, and larger organic particles and dead animals continually rain down from above. For predators, the bottom mud abounds with small animals—large numbers of individuals, if not of species.

Ponds generally are basin-shaped. Fine sediments constantly settle along the sloping sides and in the center. Thick, rich blankets of organic sediment do not make the best of habitats for most pond organisms; in fact, many pond animals suffocate in such surroundings. There are a few organisms, however, that are adapted to this kind of habitat and are not found elsewhere in great numbers.

The burrowers of the bottom

Deep in the soil on land you would expect to find roundworms, or nematodes, and segmented worms. In a pond bottom, too, microscopic nematodes are often present in enormous numbers, and there may be almost as many segmented worms. Both types of worms thrive in regions that are thick with sediment and that have diminished supplies of oxygen. The nematodes are burrowers that probe their way through the mud with needlelike bodies. They wriggle slowly back and forth as they go along but increase their speed if they come to a region where the particles of sediment are not tightly packed.

Some fresh-water segmented worms, or oligochaetes, make burrows with cylindrical extensions rising above the bottom. They live and feed head downward in the burrow, passing quantities of mud through their digestive tracts and finally excreting it from a pore at the end of their bodies, which stick far out of the tubes. From the mud they extract nourishing organic matter. A bottom infested with worms of this sort—*Tubifex* is a common type—is a striking sight, for thousands of long swaying shapes writhe about, their movements causing some exchange of water in their burrows.

Other kinds of worms burrow freely through the bottom, feeding on detritus as they go along. One variety, *Chaetogaster*, is carnivorous and feeds upon smaller worms, small crustaceans, and burrowing insect larvae, mostly midges.

More bottom dwellers

There are also other burrowers, including mussels, snails, copepods, nymphs of some insects, and midge and horse-fly larvae. In addition to animals that burrow into the bottom, there are creatures that sprawl on top of it—certain mayfly nymphs, dragonfly nymphs, crayfish, isopods, snails, and flatworms.

A few larger animals get most of their food from the bottom. Snapping and musk turtles capture and scavenge what they can. Suckers, catfish, and carp are well adapted to rooting about and seek food either with sensitive *barbels*, fleshy sensory organs that hang like whiskers under their mouths, or with mouths that are directed straight down.

By far the greatest activity in the bottom goes unseen: that of bacteria, fungi, and protozoans, which live successfully with little or no oxygen. Their activities are of inesti-

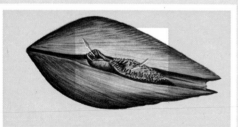

Here is a close-up view of a fresh-water clam's siphons.
Water enters through one fringed, slitlike opening, or
siphon, and leaves by another smaller opening just
above it. Suspended food particles are captured on the
mucus-coated gills (the orange areas within the siphons).
The same water currents also bring the clam oxygen
and carry away its waste products.

mable importance to the biological balance of a pond, for they alter much of the organic matter that falls to the bottom and release nutrients into the water that otherwise would remain locked in the sediment.

Animal strainers

Some of the animals of a muddy bottom, and many of those of a cleaner bottom, are filter feeders: they draw in water from which they extract food particles. Perhaps the most striking example of a filter feeder is the fresh-water mussel. This mollusk, which actually is a true clam, pulls itself along through the sediment by extending a blade-shaped muscular foot that swells at the tip and then contracts. At the opposite end of its shell, elevated above the bottom, two fleshy openings, or *siphons*, lead to the interior. If you look through a magnifying glass at a mussel in an aquarium, you will notice that water flows into the larger, fringed lower siphon, and out of the smaller, slightly longer siphon.

The inner surface of the fleshy mantle that surrounds the mussel's body, the surface of the body itself, and the gills are covered with cilia similar to those of ciliate protozoans. The cilia beat in such a way as to force water through pores in the gills. As the water flows through, mucus secreted by the gills traps particles of detritus, zooplankton, and phytoplankton in thick, sticky sheets. Other cilia on both sides of the animal pass the sheets of mucus toward the mouth, which lies between two leaflike flaps on each side. The filtered water is exhaled through the upper siphon. The quantities of plankton and suspended detritus removed from a pond by fresh-water mussels are truly enormous, especially when four or five of these mollusks are crowded together in one square foot of pond bottom.

The far smaller pill clams, pea clams, and fingernail clams have feeding habits similar to those of the fresh-water mussels, and they can also filter tremendous amounts of detritus. Occasionally as many as five hundred individuals may be packed in a square foot of pond bottom. You can hold dozens of these little clams in the palm of your hand, but it is best not to try to keep them, for they usually die rather quickly in home aquariums. Mussels live quite well in aquariums, although it is almost impossible to feed them adequately; and you must immediately remove those that die, before they decay and pollute the water.

181

There are multitudes of smaller filter feeders on every exposed surface in a pond. All the peritrich protozoans, which may grow singly or in colonies, strain and tug at their filamentous attachments as they pull in suspended particles with their strong ciliary currents. Sometimes there are so many individuals of the larger protozoan *Stentor* that they cover sticks and pebbles with a thick coating. Tube-dwelling rotifers also create ciliary whirlpools that bring water-borne matter their way. Bryozoan "moss animals," such as the massive *Pectinatella* colonies, strain quantities of water wherever they grow. Sponges are among the most effective animal strainers, with their thousands of pores and flagellated chambers.

There are many other kinds of filter feeders in a pond, but none are more active than certain members of the zooplankton. A particular group of copepods (calanoids), ostracods, and cladoceran water fleas feed only by sifting organisms and material from the water. The feeding appendages of some of these small crustaceans have hairs so fine and so closely spaced that they effectively filter out individual bacteria. Calanoids use a highly complex system of antennae and other appendages to bring a stream of water into their filtering apparatus at a rate of over one thousand beats a minute.

Stentor, shown here fifteen times life size, are trumpet-shaped protozoans which are found both as free-swimming individuals and, as here, clustered together in a crowded colony on a bit of pond substrate. The wide end of the animal is fringed with a circle of cilia which set up currents to sweep food organisms into the mouth opening. The bright green coloration of most of the *Stentor* shown here results from the presence of symbiotic algae living within the animals' bodies.

The crowded world of the plankton

Perhaps it is not accurate to speak of the world of the plankton as a microhabitat, yet to succeed in it each tiny planktonic organism must have special adaptations not possessed by the larger surface swimmers or bottom dwellers.

Taking just the copepod crustaceans alone, you can find several species occupying a variety of ecological niches. There are those that swim about very rapidly, seizing food whenever they come across it. These are known as cyclopoids, of which the common *Cyclops* is the best known example. Then there are the harpacticoids, which live in the bottom and between sand grains in the shoreline itself, and there are the filter-feeding calanoids.

Direct competition between two species seldom occurs in nature, for if it did, one of the two would gradually be replaced by the more successful. There would be no stalemate. The establishing of a special way of life is the finding of an ecological niche, and every planktonic organism in the pond is a specialist.

If you are lucky enough to have the use of a microscope in your pond studies, if only for a while, you will come across a multitude of interesting and distinctive planktonic organisms, only a few of which can be described in this book.

Pectinatella colonies consist of thousands of minute bryozoans, or moss animals, embedded in the surface of a mass of jelly that sometimes reaches the size of the three colonies shown here. Each colony is formed in a single season from a statoblast—a kind of cold- or drought-resistant body—no more than a twenty-fifth of an inch in diameter. The colonies disintegrate with the coming of cold weather, releasing statoblasts from which new colonies will arise in the spring.

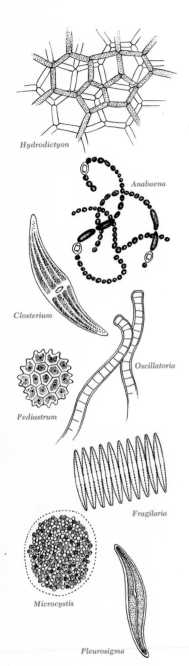

Hydrodictyon

Anabaena

Closterium

Oscillatoria

Pediastrum

Fragilaria

Microcystis

Pleurosigma

The tiny drifting plants

Blue-green algae, the most primitive photosynthetic plants, are represented by a number of different forms in the plankton, many of which give the water unpleasant tastes and odors if they become too plentiful. A blue-green alga that commonly colors ponds is *Microcystis. Anabaena,* a common variety, appears in ponds in straight, knotted, or spiral filaments, each a distinct species. As we have mentioned, some blue-green algae are not that color at all, but brownish or even reddish. One kind, *Gloeotrichia,* is composed of many tapering rays arranged in a star-shaped pattern; the overall appearance under low magnification is a brownish-green sphere. At times this alga may choke the water with its numbers.

The planktonic diatoms are beautifully constructed microscopic plants with their boxlike outer skeletons composed of glassy silica. When a diatom divides, the two halves separate, with the lid forming a new bottom and the old bottom becoming a lid with a new bottom. It is easy to see that this cannot continue indefinitely, for with each division the two resulting cells are smaller. When a minimum size is reached, a kind of sexual reproduction takes place: two diatoms shed their silica boxes, join together, and go into a brief resting stage. After this a new, much larger shell is produced, and the whole process of division starts over again.

There are pond diatoms of all shapes and sizes. One of the most attractive you may find in your plankton tow, although it usually lives on the bottom, is *Pleurosigma,* which is long and spindle-shaped, with one end twisted to the right and the other to the left.

Plant geometry

Planktonic green algae are among the most beautiful organisms in ponds. Their brilliant color is often enhanced by lenslike transparent protein granules that refract light passing through the cell. Desmids, composed of two halves joined together by a narrow bridge, will probably be the first algae to catch your eye under a microscope. A desmid cell usually has toothed spines, projections, or other sculpturings. The graceful crescent-shaped *Closterium* is a common form.

184

A colony of green cells, *Pediastrum*, forms a radial design, a disk of geometrically arranged cells with two short spines on the outer row. When you come across this plant for the first time, you will be amazed and delighted by its symmetry and beauty.

One of the oddest green plants is *Hydrodictyon*, known as water net. Thousands of cells form a green veil over the water in shallow parts of the pond. When you examine the plant closely, you will see that a true three-dimensional net is formed; the spaces are bordered by five or six cells, and the cells always meet and join together in threes.

Plants that swim

Then there are the swimming algae, or flagellates, many of which can just as well be classified within the animal kingdom. In fact, they are classified as Protista, simple organisms that possess features of both plants and animals. *Euglena* has already been mentioned, but there are many more. One that is very much like *Euglena*, *Trachelomonas*, lives in a tiny bottle-shaped flask constructed of cellulose, the universal plant structural material. Some species are red, owing to the presence of iron compounds in the cellulose. Depending upon the species, the flask may have knobs, spines, bumps, ridges, and so on. The organism extends its flagellum through the neck of the flask and swims rapidly along.

Phacus, another relative of *Euglena*, looks like a brilliant animated leaf. It is broad, flat, or twisted, with a flagellum and a bright red eyespot that helps orient the photosynthetic flagellate to the light. As an individual swims along with a rotating motion, the off-center eyespot is alternately exposed to and then shielded from a light source, and the cell constantly corrects its swimming so that it is always moving toward the light. You can prove this without any elaborate equipment. Simply take a container of pond water in which there are a number of green flagellates, and place it in a window. Close to the top there will soon be a green line composed of swimming cells adhering to the side of the glass nearest the sunlight.

Euglena itself comes in many sizes and shapes. One huge one has a flagellum that is very small in relation to its large, twisted body, and so moves very slowly. The surface of this species has many tiny knobs arranged in spiral rows.

The light band across the middle of crescent-shaped *Closterium* cells (*top*, magnified three hundred times) identifies them as desmids, a group of algae that occur in an almost limitless variety of attractive forms. *Phacus* (*bottom*, magnified six hundred times) is typical of the pond's chlorophyll-bearing flagellates.

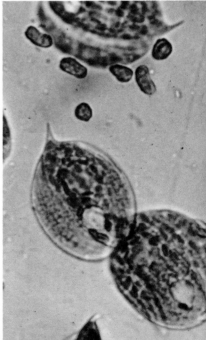

SMALL-GAME HUNT

To the person whose curiosity is stirred by the world of
nature, the pond offers a unique and very special appeal. Many
of us will never have the chance to visit a coral reef or a
tropical jungle, but nearly everyone has access to a pond. And
any pond is the home of a multitude of creatures, which, if
generally smaller and less flamboyantly colored than the
denizens of the reef and the jungle, are by no means less
interesting.

Indeed, much of the attraction of a pond lies in its very
compactness, in the fact that it is a complete, self-contained
world small enough to be studied and appreciated in its
entirety. Taken singly, its inhabitants include some of the most
fascinating creatures to be found anywhere; taken as a
community, they display a remarkable and sometimes baffling
web of interdependencies that can offer enough engrossing
riddles to last anyone a lifetime.

The only really essential equipment for exploring this strange
and still largely uncharted realm, besides an inquiring mind, is
pictured below: eyes and hands. The rest, such as the dip net
on the right and the other gear shown on the next two pages,
can be classed as luxuries and refinements.

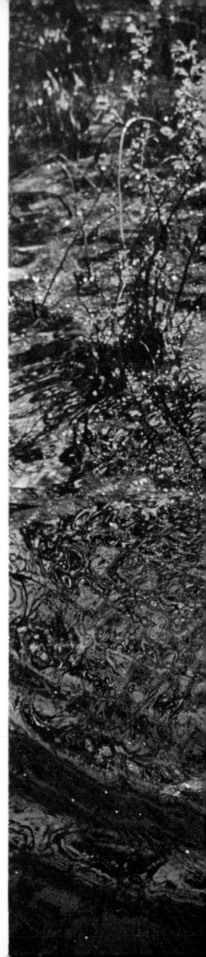

A fine-meshed net (above left), *towed slowly behind a boat, will yield a highly concentrated sample of the pond's plankton population. A small dredge* (center) *can be used to bring up debris from the bottom. An ordinary minnow seine* (right) *will capture fish, amphibians, and other larger pond inhabitants.*

Pond study can be as simple or as elaborate as you care to make it, but even quite detailed investigations can be conducted without much of an investment. The equipment shown in action on these two pages is of more or less professional quality, yet all of it, with the exception of the microscope at the lower right, can be replaced by inexpensive homemade substitutes. Even a simple microscope of good quality can be had for a surprisingly low price. You will need books, but these can come from your library or can be purchased in inexpensive editions. In the Appendix of this book you will find some suggestions on how to get started as a "pond watcher"—and once started, chances are good that you will have embarked upon a lifetime journey into this wondrous underwater world.

One of the most useful collecting tools of all is an ordinary white-bottomed enamel pan (right) in which a handful of vegetation, dead leaves, or the like can be picked over for insect larvae, snails, leeches, and other organisms. A stereomicroscope (far right), if available, is helpful for observing smaller creatures.

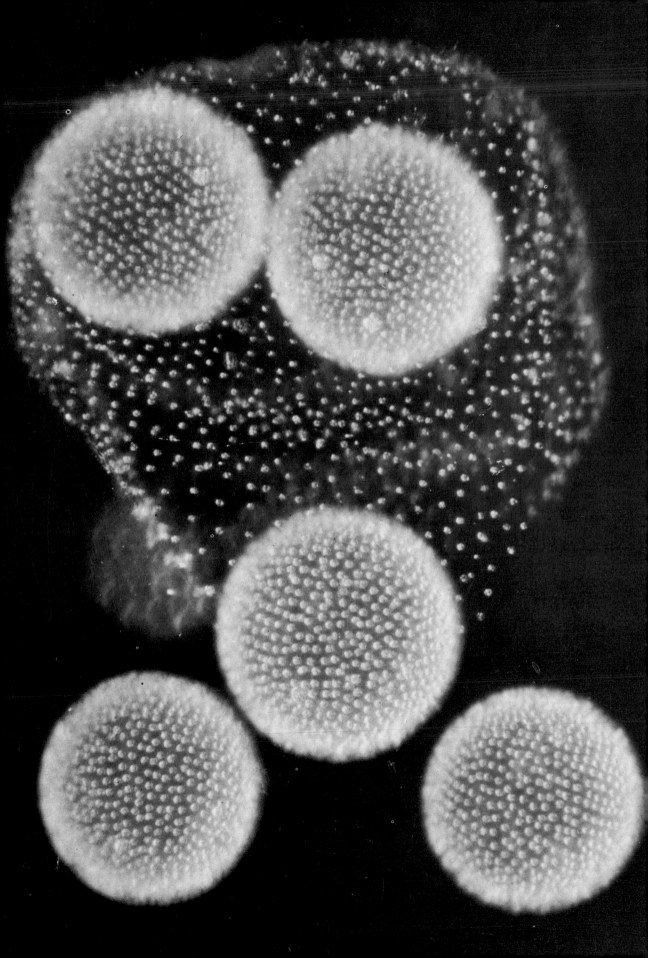

The large colonial flagellate *Volvox* can reproduce
asexually by forming new colonies within its hollow
body; as the parent colony disintegrates, the new
colonies take up independent existence.

One of the strangest sights you may come across under
the microscope is something that looks like a bush made out
of transparent wineglasses. If you look closely, you will notice that each wineglass contains a single cell with two
flagella. The glass, or vase, is constructed out of cellulose
and does not decay easily. Often you can find the glassy
bush of *Dinobryon* without seeing any of the living cells inside.

A living globe

Volvox is an organism that has been famous since the time
of its discovery by Leeuwenhoek. As a matter of fact, it is
not clear even today whether it is a single organism or a
colony of many single cells. This large spherical plant-
animal, easily visible to the naked eye, is composed of
up to a thousand cells, each with an eyespot and two flagella.
The cells are connected by fine coordinating fibers that run
through a gelatinous casing. *Volvox* does not simply stay in
one spot, spinning like a top, but tumbles along through the
water like an animated ball. It reproduces by forming new
spherical colonies within the parent. After the daughter colonies are grown, they burst through the wall of the parent,
which then swims irregularly and dies. *Volvox* also reproduces sexually by means of sperm-fertilized cells. Its tough,
spiny eggs can resist the cold and ice of winter.

Still another group of flagellates, the dinoflagellates, are
common in pond water. Some have ornamented, sculptured
outer skeletons composed of cellulose. Dinoflagellates move
by means of two flagella, one extending out and the other
lying in a groove that extends around the cell. Some have
spines; others are rounded and smooth.

SPERM BUNDLE   EGG

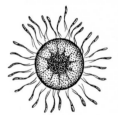

During sexual reproduction, a *Volvox* colony (*top drawing*) can produce two types of germ cells: large female cells, or eggs, and much
smaller but more numerous male cells, or sperms. The male cells,
which are motile, seek out a female cell (*second drawing*), and a
single male cell unites with it, forming a zygote. Still within the parent
colony, the zygote forms a tough, cold-resistant cyst (*third drawing*)
which survives the winter, though the parent colony does not. When
spring arrives, the cyst breaks open (*bottom drawing*) and releases a
new *Volvox* colony.

191

The world of zooplankton

Every zone of the pond has its characteristic kinds of rotifers; the species shown here is *Asplanchna*, an inhabitant of the pond's plankton community. *Asplanchna* is a giant as rotifers go, reaching an overall length of about a thirty-second of an inch. The circular bodies visible through the animal's nearly transparent cuticle are developing embryos.

There are not so many different kinds of animal plankton in fresh water as in the seas, but there are enough for a lifetime of study. The smallest are the one-celled protozoans. Relatively few protozoans, however, are typically planktonic in their habits, unless some of the flagellates just described are considered to be protozoans, an idea zoologists accept and botanists deny. Most of the protozoans live close to the bottom, or among mats of algae, or in floating detritus.

Some species of rotifers are not much larger than the protozoans, but most of them are active as members of the plankton. Rotifers have always been a microscopist's delight. They are common and are easy to keep and study. Most have two ciliated crowns around the head, a red eyespot, furiously chomping jaws, a telescopic foot with two pointed toes, and clear internal anatomy. A few species are fixed permanently in tubes, but most are very active, always busy feeding, swimming, or changing position.

Keratella, one of the smaller rotifers, is encased in a spiny symmetrical shell which probably has at least two advantages: it discourages predators, and it increases the surface area of the animal in relation to its volume, thereby helping it to remain suspended in the water. Spines in both plants and animals are excellent flotation devices.

The large, highly transparent *Asplanchna* is so thoroughly adapted to its planktonic way of life that it lacks the two-toed foot possessed by almost all other rotifers. It is quite possible to look inside *Asplanchna* and see the workings of its internal jaws, food in its stomach, and tiny developing embryos.

Another odd planktonic species, *Conochilus*, has a colonial way of life. It is composed of dozens of individuals, all held together by a gelatinous case that envelops the tips of their tails. The colony tumbles along rapidly, propelled by cilia that beat around the head of each individual. If one is accidentally separated from the others, it continues to live successfully. Like all rotifers, it can produce more individuals from unfertilized eggs and form a new colony without difficulty.

Gastrotrichs are animals distantly related to rotifers. Though never particularly plentiful, they are common enough to be seen in almost every pond collection. They are very small creatures, rather wormlike, with bristles and overlapping scales. Gastrotrichs are more common on the bottom and in detritus than in the plankton, but you can occasionally find them in the plankton too.

The smallest shrimps

Usually the most common members of the zooplankton are crustaceans. In the ocean, copepod crustaceans are the most abundant, but this is seldom the case in fresh water. Copepods such as *Cyclops* are always about, but they usually do not compete in numbers with the cladoceran water fleas.

One cladoceran, *Daphnia*, is as interesting to look at under a microscope as a rotifer, for it is just as transparent and much more complex. Its single anterior eye is made up of many smaller eyes, which give it a beaded appearance. Above the front part of its intestine you can see a completely transparent, rapidly pulsating bubble—the heart. If you look through your microscope very closely indeed, you can even see the colorless blood streaming through the heart.

Any sample of pond water is virtually certain to contain at least a few copepods such as *Cyclops*, shown here with two rotifers and several star-shaped clusters of *Asterionella* diatoms. *Cyclops* derives its name from the one-eyed giant of Greek mythology, for, like its namesake, it has a single eye situated between its antennae.

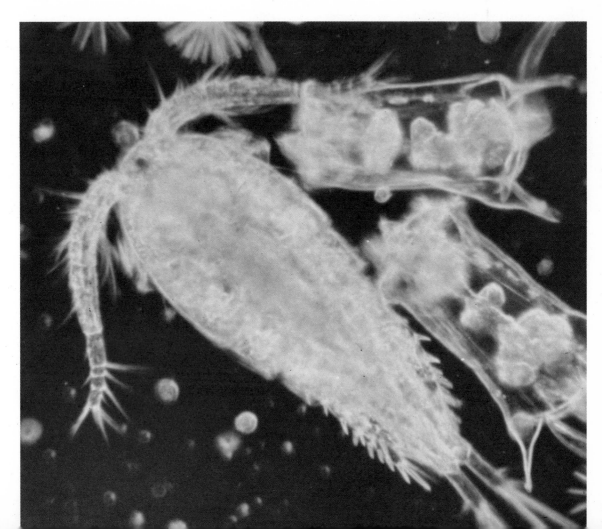

Daphnia is usually described as a typical cladoceran, but *Leptodora*, with its weird, elongated body, and the back-swimming water flea are two other very different types.

Within the antennae with which a cladoceran swims are powerful muscles that are visible if you adjust the light of your microscope carefully. In addition, toward the rear of the animal there is a large single kicking "leg" which the crea-

This eighth-of-an-inch ostracod (*above left*) looks a little like a cross between a clam and a shrimp; it is a crustacean with a bivalve shell from which several pairs of swimming appendages protrude. When water conditions favor their reproduction, ostracods can blanket portions of a pond's bottom (*above right*).

ture thrusts out when it browses through more solid material.

Close to the bottom of the pond are ostracods, strange little crustaceans that resemble highly animated clams. Although they do have a hinged two-valved shell, their bodies inside are shrimplike. An ostracod's shell is hardened and thickened by a limy compound, so that you can see very little of the animal itself except for its jointed, kicking legs. Small water mites live in the same kind of habitat as ostracods and even resemble them when viewed without magnification. With their eight bristled legs they swim along rapidly and smoothly.

194

Other members of the plankton

Early in spring, tiny larval fish join these invertebrates and might be considered members of the plankton. Young largemouth bass develop in transparent eggs cemented to pebbles close to shore. Because of their heavy yolk sacs, they remain in their nests for a while after hatching. After the yolk is

In the spring, the pond's plankton community may include swarms of newly hatched fish larvae. The larva shown below is about a quarter of an inch long.

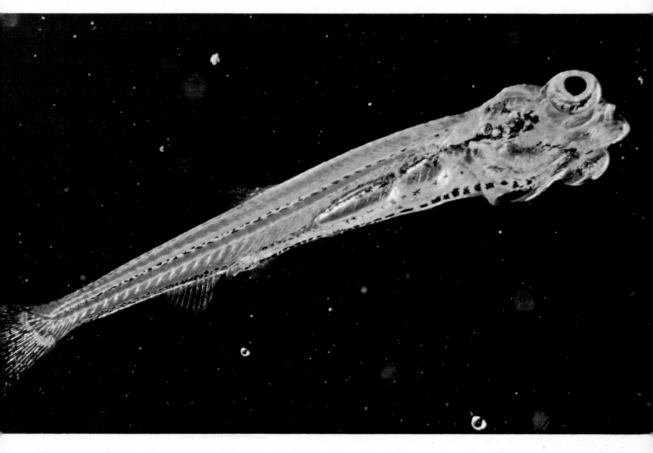

absorbed, the small fish begin active feeding and move close to the surface in warm, shallow water, where they swim about in schools. Their food at this time, and for weeks to come, consists of nothing but plankton, both plant and animal. At this stage the tiny larvae are not very much larger than most members of the animal plankton, and smaller than some.

Two insect members of the plankton, the phantom midge larva and a swimming caddisfly larva, have already been mentioned. Not many other insects are found in the plankton.

The hidden life of the soil

Where does a pond stop? Precisely at the water line? A moment's thought will tell you that the surrounding soil, as well as the bottom itself, is saturated with water.

The organisms that are present close to a pond's edge are not typical of soil farther inland; they are usually found only in this specific zone of transition, which the ecologist calls an *ecotone*. As you go away from the pond, the amount of moisture in the soil decreases, and you begin to find earthworms, mole crickets, moles, cicada nymphs, and so on.

If a pond has a very muddy shore, the forms of life in this zone are restricted to those that can tolerate fine silt and low oxygen content. Here you will find such organisms as bacteria, roundworms, small segmented worms, and certain midge larvae. Some ponds do not have muddy shores, however—at least not around their whole margin. Often you will find sandy stretches with very little silt. Such a miniature beach will reward you with a number of interesting discoveries.

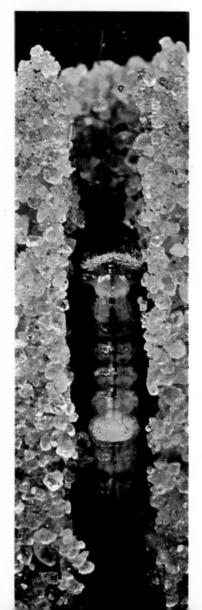

The wet, sandy shores of a pond will usually contain burrows of predatory tiger beetle larvae. The burrow shown here has been cut away to reveal a larva; all that you would normally see would be an inconspicuous hole in the sand, perhaps plugged by the top of the larva's head.

Animals among the sand grains

In the top layers of damp sand, among bits of vegetable debris, you may be able to find a dark, deeply segmented insect larva. It may not look very interesting by day, but if you visit the same spot at night you will see numerous bright little flashes of light in the wet sand. Reach down and scoop up what is there, and you will have caught a glowworm; this is the larva of the familiar flying beetle, the firefly or lightning bug. The light emitted by both larvae and adults is in one of the most efficient forms known: it is nearly completely heatless. The insects generate light by means of an enzyme, making it possible to combine a substance known as *luciferin* with oxygen. Presumably the light is useful to the adults during the mating season, but biologists do not know why the immature larvae produce it.

During the daytime, you may notice small round holes in the sand, only a few inches from the water's edge. Some of them may seem to have an iridescent plug which, as you move close, disappears below. If you very carefully excavate the hole, you will find an elongated insect larva with a curious humped back and a grotesque flat head equipped

196

with sicklelike jaws. This is the larva of a tiger beetle, which is a common resident in the wet sand of pond shores. It rests with its head level with the surface. When another insect runs by, the larva reaches out and grabs it. It maintains a secure anchorage in its hole with the bumps, or tubercles, on its back; these also enable it to go up and down its burrow quickly.

Dig a hole in the wet sand not far from the water's edge; it will quickly fill with water seeping through the sand. If you take some of this water and strain it through a fine cloth, you should collect a number of organisms that live in the water between sand grains. These animals usually are elongated and able to slip through narrow spaces with ease. They are roundworms, segmented worms, rotifers, gastrotrichs, water bears, and highly specialized harpacticoid copepods.

Here is a victim's-eye view of the tiger beetle larva's head. The scraggly covering of white hairs helps protect the creature from the direct rays of the sun. The adult beetle also has long sicklelike jaws and is just as predatory as the larva.

Bacteria, concentrated mostly in the upper inch of sand, are the most numerous organisms. Many millions of them may inhabit a cubic half inch of wet sand. In the same volume, there can also be several thousand protozoans, a dozen or so rotifers, and a few copepods and other organisms. Altogether the sand grains shelter a rather crowded community but a flourishing one.

Exploring the pond world

We are, by nature, explorers, but not all of us can go to far-away lands, to the depths of the oceans, or into space. The odd thing is that man has by-passed so many obvious places in his search for the new. And no one realizes this fact more than the biologist with an interest in fresh-water life. He will tell you that in even the smallest pond you can find many things that presently cannot be explained. Each year professional journals are filled with new studies of fresh-water organisms. Some pond animals have not even been named by biologists, much less studied.

The organisms described here are but a very few of those that may be found in any pond in your neighborhood. A pond is accessible to anyone, and knowledge of its inhabitants can be acquired with nothing but a pair of eyes and an interested, inquisitive mind. Nets, magnifying instruments, and glassware are all luxuries. A source of information about what you observe is essential, however. Books open the door to the pond world, and you will find many that lead you far beyond the brief introduction presented here.

Good luck in your explorations. A final word of warning: once you become a pond hunter, you may remain one all your life.

Beneath its surface, a pond harbors a miniature world which in many ways is a model of the larger world beyond its shores. To anyone who will take the time to stop and look into its waters, a pond offers a vivid panorama of the living world.

Appendix

Ponds in Our National Parks
and Wildlife Refuges

Spreading across America is a splendid system of national parks, monuments, and wildlife refuges, maintained and operated by the Department of the Interior. The parks and monuments, administered by the department's National Park Service, preserve sites of special scenic or historical interest and provide facilities for human recreation and enjoyment. In the wildlife refuges, administered by the department's Fish and Wildlife Service, human interests come second: these areas are intended primarily for the shelter and protection of our native birds and animals. Throughout the system, you will find ponds of every description, in natural, unspoiled settings.

The majority of these ponds are very much like the ones described in this book, since ponds exhibit a remarkable constancy throughout the country. There are exceptions, however, and fascinating ones—the thermal pools of Yellowstone National Park, where the water remains close to the boiling point; the brine-filled hollows of Death Valley National Monument; the frigid tundra ponds of Mount McKinley National Park. All these support living communities adapted to their unusual conditions.

So many parks and refuges contain ponds that this book could not describe them all, but those discussed here will provide a representative sampling of the many such areas administered by the Department of the Interior. It is hoped that you will take the opportunity to visit some of them and to enjoy their ponds.

WHOOPING CRANE

Aransas National Wildlife Refuge (Texas)
This wildlife refuge, fringing the Gulf coast of Texas, is perhaps the most famous of all, since it is the winter home of the most publicized and one of the least populous of all native American birds, the whooping cranes. In addition to the celebrated whoopers, a rich variety of other wading birds pass the winter in the refuge's seven ponds. The refuge is open to visitors throughout the year, although the area frequented by the forty-odd whooping cranes still in existence is strictly off-limits.

Bitter Lake National Wildlife Refuge (New Mexico)
Bitter Lake includes some eighteen pothole ponds formed by an unusual process. Underground water dissolved gypsum layers in the soil, and the domes of the resulting hollows eventually

202

caved in to form ponds varying in depth from fifteen to nearly one hundred feet. The high salinity of the water in these ponds supports the growth of marine algae, over five hundred miles from the sea. Bitter Lake is a happy hunting ground for bird watchers: on nearly any day during the winter months, from fifty to sixty species can be observed within the refuge.

Cape Hatteras National Seashore (North Carolina)
In wet weather, more than a hundred ponds are scattered through this seventy-mile chain of barrier islands extending along the Carolina coast; in dry weather, the number shrinks to a few dozen. Periodic invasions of salt water into normally fresh-water ponds are common. Despite the changeable conditions, or perhaps because of them, plant and animal life is both richly varied and abundant. Although Hatteras is separated from the mainland, the presence of the salamander *Amphiuma,* which cannot tolerate salt water, suggests that a connection once existed. Cape Hatteras National Seashore includes Pea Island National Wildlife Refuge.

Carolina Sandhills National Wildlife Refuge (South Carolina)
This refuge contains twenty-seven fresh-water ponds, all man-made, varying in size from one to sixty acres and ranging in depth from less than a foot to eighteen feet. The pond life is highly typical of ponds everywhere, and a large percentage of the plants and animals pictured in this book can be observed here. A feature of the refuge is a self-guiding nature trail along which visitors can enjoy many of the refuge's attractions. With written permission from the refuge office, hikers may visit other parts of the refuge's 46,000 acres.

BLACK DUCK

Clarence Rhode National Wildlife Range (Alaska)
How many ponds here? It is unlikely that anyone will ever count them to find out: estimates suggest that the range's 1,800,000 acres include over a million ponds, ranging from miniatures only a few yards across to shallow lakes fifteen miles long. The ponds are summer breeding grounds for tens of thousands of geese and ducks and numerous species of other waterfowl.

Columbia National Wildlife Refuge (Washington)
The Columbia Refuge includes over one hundred ponds, which collectively illustrate how ponds that are more or less side by side can vary radically in their animal and plant populations. They host a variety of wildlife, including muskrats, beavers, raccoons, skunks, badgers, and over 160 species of birds. Some of Columbia's ponds teem with fish, and others contain no fish at all. Why? The degree of acidity varies from pond to pond;

perhaps this is sufficient to make subtle differences in food webs that encourage fish proliferation in some ponds and discourage it in others.

Everglades National Park (Florida)

Located at the very tip of the Florida peninsula, the Everglades offers exotic wildlife that cannot be found anywhere else in the country. Among the common reptiles are alligators; snakes; and red-bellied, snapping, and stinkpot, or soft-shelled, turtles. The park includes countless ponds, some of them created by fire—hollows formed from the burning of peat—and some produced by alligator digging. Water life of every sort is abundant here, although its concentration in ponds varies with season.

ALLIGATOR

Great Swamp National Wildlife Refuge (New Jersey)

This wildlife refuge, just forty miles due west of Times Square, is an important stopover point for migratory waterfowl. Six ponds are included within its bounds, which will eventually embrace over five thousand acres of unspoiled wilderness located in the center of one of the most densely populated areas in the country. In addition to birds, reptiles and amphibians are plentiful here: eight species of turtles and twenty-one of frogs, toads, and salamanders can be found in Great Swamp.

Gulf Island National Wildlife Refuge (Mississippi)

Located approximately ten miles from the mainland, this refuge can be reached only by boat. It includes about forty ponds, the waters of which range from slightly brackish to a saltiness near that of seawater. As a result, the plant and animal populations are an odd mixture: familiar fresh-water forms such as cattails and raccoons share living quarters with such marine forms as black drum and flounder. The islands are closed to the public during the fall and winter months, to minimize disturbance to the great flocks of water birds that nest there during that part of the year.

Lacreek National Wildlife Refuge (South Dakota)

Lacreek contains twelve fresh-water impoundments designed specifically to accommodate migratory waterfowl, but housing a wide variety of familiar pond animals as well, including beavers, raccoons, snapping turtles, and bullfrogs. Common plants include sedges, cattails, bulrushes, spike rush, and pondweed. Over two hundred species of birds have been identified within the refuge. An attempt is being made to establish a nesting colony of the once nearly extinct trumpeter swan. The impoundments can be visited at all times of the year, but visitors must first obtain permits from the refuge manager.

204

Olympic National Park (Washington)

Olympic National Park includes dozens of ponds, mostly of glacial origin and ranging in elevation from near sea level to over a mile above. Many of the ponds at higher altitudes display striking color contrasts owing to vegetation and silt deposits. Among the park's prime animal attractions is the Roosevelt elk, which is often found in numbers around the higher ponds.

Savannah National Wildlife Refuge (South Carolina)

The thirteen ponds included in this refuge, ranging in size from twenty-five acres to nearly five hundred, are connected to the tidal portion of the Savannah River, and thus have daily tides of from six to nine feet. No less than 212 species of birds, including many waterfowl, have been identified within the refuge. During the summer white ibises and purple gallinules are commonly seen, and the refuge is an important resting and feeding place for thousands of ducks. No hunting is permitted here, but the ponds are open to fishermen from March 15 to October 25, and offer bluegill, largemouth bass, bowfin, catfish, carp, crappie, and gar.

BLACK CRAPPIE

Sherburne National Wildlife Refuge (Minnesota)

One of the newest of our refuges, Sherburne National Wildlife Refuge contains about a thousand ponds, ranging in type from prairie potholes to typical woodland ponds. Many are the remains of what were once bog lakes. Common birds include ducks, herons, bitterns, and the short-billed marsh wren.

Yellowstone National Park (Wyoming, Montana, Idaho)

The oldest and still the largest of our national parks, Yellowstone is best known for its geysers, hot springs, and bears, but it also contains several hundred ponds of all sizes and types. Many of these ponds are the result of beaver activity, and Yellowstone is a fine place to observe these interesting mammals in action. Muskrats, moose, many kinds of ducks, Canada geese, and trumpeter swans can also be seen. Even the hot springs are not entirely devoid of life: though the water is near the boiling point, certain primitive algae thrive in them.

Yosemite National Park (California)

The wild beauty for which Yosemite National Park is noted is the result of glacial action, and among the work of the glaciers are several dozen ponds. Some are quite shallow, and others are deep enough to show temperature layering of the water, an effect more common in larger bodies of water. Frogs, toads, and salamanders are commonly found. Yosemite is a hiker's paradise with trails leading up to many scenic alpine ponds.

What a Fish Sees

What does a fish see when it surveys its underwater world? No one can say for certain, of course, since one cannot get inside a fish's brain, but it is possible to make some deductions based on laboratory studies of fish behavior and on what we know about the nature of light.

First, we know from laboratory experiments that fish see in color, although not necessarily in quite the same way that humans do. The black bass, for example, sees colors about as you would if you were wearing yellow sunglasses. Fish are probably rather near-sighted, seeing objects at close range more clearly than those farther away. And some species, at least, apparently have well-developed depth perception.

A fish can see objects on the shore, too. Why is it that you seldom see a fish from the bank of a pond? Except for those sunfish and bass that are guarding nests close to shore, all you see is a cloud of mud rising from the bottom where a fish, with a sudden burst of speed, darts away to deeper water. The explanation lies in the fact that a fish usually sees you long before you are aware of it. But how can a fish see you if it lies below an overhanging bank, not in your direct line of sight? To understand that it does see you in this position, you need to know something of elementary optics. Light passes through a transparent medium, such as air, water, or glass, at a speed governed by the composition and density of the medium. Water is more dense than air, and light is slowed and deflected when it enters water. This accounts for the apparent bending of a stick when you place it at an angle half in the water and half in air. The greater the angle, the greater the apparent bending. There is, however, a limit to the angle of refraction, beyond which light, instead of being refracted, is reflected—bounced off the underside of the water surface, as though it were the surface of a mirror. This critical angle is 48.8 degrees.

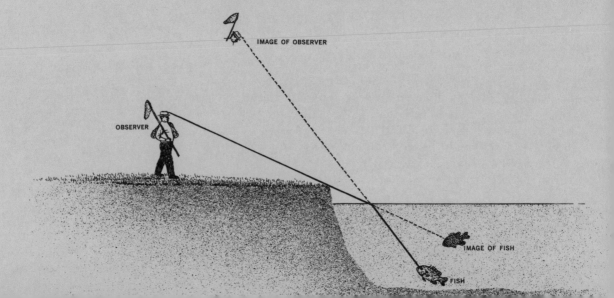

IMAGE OF OBSERVER

OBSERVER

IMAGE OF FISH

FISH

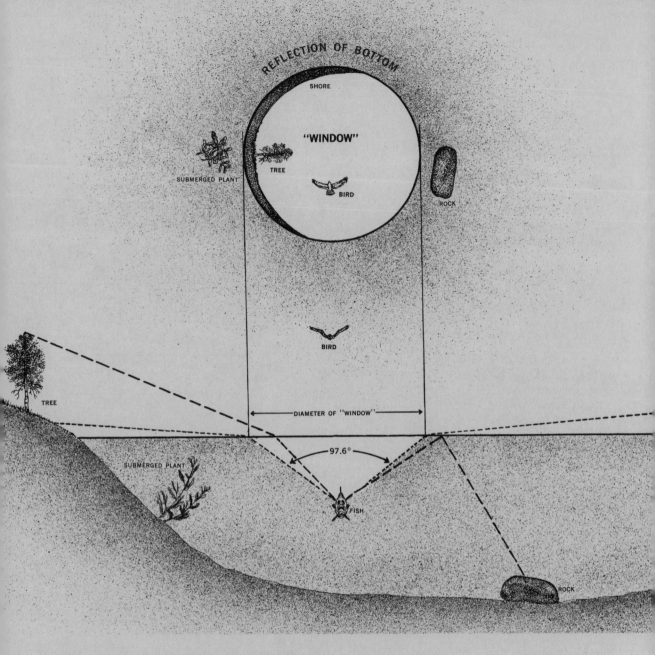

Thus, a fish looking up toward the surface in quiet water sees the shoreline through a sort of transparent window, 97.6 degrees wide. Beyond this window he sees mirror images of objects (such as the rock in the diagram) within the pond. The secret, then, of approaching such a fish is to keep yourself out of the "window" portion of its visual field. In this way, the fish will not be able to see you, though of course you will not be able to see the fish, either. At any rate, this is a useful way of getting to a likely fishing spot without frightening away too many fish.

207

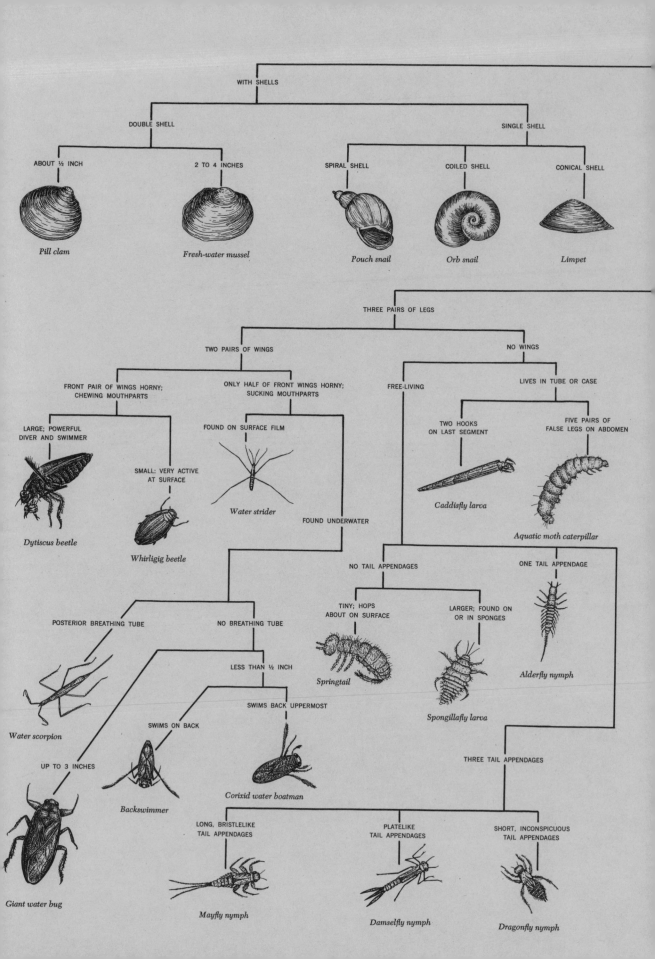

WITH SHELLS

DOUBLE SHELL

SINGLE SHELL

ABOUT ½ INCH

2 TO 4 INCHES

SPIRAL SHELL

COILED SHELL

CONICAL SHELL

Pill clam

Fresh-water mussel

Pouch snail

Orb snail

Limpet

THREE PAIRS OF LEGS

TWO PAIRS OF WINGS

NO WINGS

FRONT PAIR OF WINGS HORNY;
CHEWING MOUTHPARTS

ONLY HALF OF FRONT WINGS HORNY;
SUCKING MOUTHPARTS

FREE-LIVING

LIVES IN TUBE OR CASE

LARGE; POWERFUL
DIVER AND SWIMMER

FOUND ON SURFACE FILM

TWO HOOKS
ON LAST SEGMENT

FIVE PAIRS OF
FALSE LEGS ON ABDOMEN

SMALL; VERY ACTIVE
AT SURFACE

Water strider

Caddisfly larva

Dytiscus beetle

FOUND UNDERWATER

Aquatic moth caterpillar

Whirligig beetle

NO TAIL APPENDAGES

ONE TAIL APPENDAGE

POSTERIOR BREATHING TUBE

NO BREATHING TUBE

TINY; HOPS
ABOUT ON SURFACE

LARGER; FOUND ON
OR IN SPONGES

LESS THAN ½ INCH

Alderfly nymph

SWIMS BACK UPPERMOST

Springtail

Water scorpion

Spongillafly larva

SWIMS ON BACK

THREE TAIL APPENDAGES

UP TO 3 INCHES

Corixid water boatman

Backswimmer

LONG, BRISTLELIKE
TAIL APPENDAGES

PLATELIKE
TAIL APPENDAGES

SHORT, INCONSPICUOUS
TAIL APPENDAGES

Giant water bug

Mayfly nymph

Damselfly nymph

Dragonfly nymph

WITHOUT SHELLS

SEGMENTED BODY

UNSEGMENTED BODY

ASYMMETRICAL

RADIAL SYMMETRY;
FREE-SWIMMING

RADIAL SYMMETRY;
SESSILE

BILATERAL SYMMETRY

ROUGH-TEXTURED;
PORES

SMOOTH;
NO PORES

ROUNDED BODY

FLATTENED BODY

Fresh-water sponge

Bryozoan colony

Fresh-water jellyfish

Hydra

Threadworm

Planarian

OBVIOUS LEGS

NO OBVIOUS LEGS

FOUR PAIRS OF LEGS

SOME APPENDAGES

NO OBVIOUS APPENDAGES

SMALL

LARGE

POSTERIOR
BREATHING TUBE

BRIGHT
RED BODY

TRANSPARENT BODY;
SILVERY AIR SACS

SMOOTH BODY;
SUCKERS

BODY WITH BRISTLES;
NO SUCKERS

Water mite

*Fisher
spider*

Mosquito larva

Midge larva

Phantom midge larva

Leech

TUBE-DWELLING

Bristle worm

MORE THAN FOUR PAIRS OF LEGS

Tubifex

LOBSTERLIKE;
SIZE TO 5 INCHES

CYLINDRICAL BODY

CLAMLIKE "SHELL"

BODY FLATTENED
TOP TO BOTTOM

BODY FLATTENED
SIDE TO SIDE

Crayfish

Copepod

Ostracod

Isopod

SWIMS WITH Y-SHAPED ANTENNAE

SWIMS WITH LEGS

Cladoceran

Amphipod

A GUIDE TO SOME COMMON POND ANIMALS

The pictorial key presented on these two pages will help you
identify some of the more common creatures you may encounter
in your pond explorations. By noting the physical characteristics
of the unknown animal and using these characteristics to trace a
path down the branching forks of the key, you will eventually reach
a "dead end" that identifies the animal. The key is limited to non-
microscopic invertebrates and shows only typical examples of the
various animal groups included. More elaborate and comprehensive
keys to aquatic plants and animals can be found in many of the
books listed in the Bibliography on page 227.

How to Learn More About a Pond

If the topics discussed in this book have interested you, the best way to further that interest is to get out and study ponds yourself. The most fruitful way to go about this is to select one pond to which you have easy access and to learn everything you can about it. By finding out how a single pond changes from season to season, and from year to year, you will build up a very good understanding of the natural history of ponds in general.

Accurate, permanent records of your observations and measurements are of utmost importance. For a start, you will want a map of your pond; you can sketch out one yourself, or you may find that your County Clerk's office can tell you where to obtain a printed map that includes your pond. If you have the use of a boat, you can plot the contour of the pond's bottom by making depth measurements with a pole or weighted line marked off in six-inch intervals.

A camera, even of the simplest type, is a useful tool in pond study. By periodically taking pictures at a series of fixed points around the pond margin, you can build up a valuable photographic record of seasonal vegetation changes and measure the rate of yearly succession. Numbered stakes, driven firmly into the ground, can serve as permanent points of reference for your picture taking.

Certain physical data can be added to your volume of information about your pond. A regular record of water temperature is useful. A simple pH test kit, sold by tropical fish dealers, will let you measure the acidity or alkalinity. A gardener's soil-testing outfit can be used to measure other chemical aspects of the water. You can measure turbidity by lowering a metal disk painted white (the top of a large tin can) and noting the depth at which it disappears from view.

Much of your attention will of course be directed toward the plants and animals that make up your pond's living community. At the least, you will want to make a census of the flora and fauna of the pond, and perhaps to keep records of the fluctuations in the abundance of various species. As a more ambitious project, you might try working out a food-web diagram for your pond. Or you may decide to concentrate on one segment of the population—the dragonflies, for example—and learn all you can about it.

The equipment you will need for your pond explorations is neither complicated nor expensive, and much of it can be homemade. Some of these devices are described on the following pages.

Basic collecting equipment

One of the most useful items for pond study is an ordinary white enamel or plastic pan. To use it, simply dump a handful or so of dead leaves and other debris from the pond bottom into the pan and then pick the pieces out one by one, examining each for eggs, animals, and other items of interest. A folding pocket magnifying glass is helpful. Specimens can be transferred from the pan to jars or vials with a pair of forceps or a medicine dropper. A plastic basting .gadget, shaped like a giant medicine dropper and available in most variety stores, is handy for picking up hard-to-catch creatures such as leeches and some insect larvae.

Weed grapple

With this device, fashioned from a short length of pipe and some stiff wire, you can bring up samples of submergent vegetation and then place them in your collecting pan for detailed examination.

Sorting screen

This device is especially useful for collecting burrowers and bottom dwellers. It consists of a simple wooden frame of any convenient size, with ordinary window screening tacked to the bottom. Place a quantity of bottom debris on the screen and slosh water over it to wash away the mud and silt.

Nets

The most useful net for pond study is a long-handled dip net, either purchased or homemade, sturdy enough to withstand a fair amount of hard use. Swept through plant tangles and along the bottom, the dip net may yield fish, amphibians, crayfish, insect larvae, and the like. An ordinary kitchen strainer, attached securely to a broom handle, is a good substitute. A six-foot minnow seine, operated by two people, allows a more wholesale sampling of the pond's fish population, but do not handle or remove fish needlessly. You can identify and count them, without harming any, simply by drawing the net in so they have only a few inches of water in which to swim; then release them by raising the net. If you are using a microscope in your pond explorations, a plankton net made of fine-mesh nylon or muslin will be useful for concentrating the microscopic plants and animals of the pond's limnetic zone.

Artificial substrates

One method of collecting sessile organisms such as sponges and bryozoans is to secure pieces of artificial substrate in various parts of the pond and simply leave them for a period of weeks or months. Pieces of wood, slate, asbestos house siding, or similar materials can be used for this purpose.

Glass-bottomed box

To observe life underwater, you will need some means of eliminating the glare and distortion caused by the water's surface. A glass-bottomed box answers this need, and can be easily made from any watertight wooden box. Cut a window in the bottom of the box and fit it with a piece of glass held in place with strips of wood and calked with waterproof putty or aquarium cement. Painting the inside of the box black will reduce glare and make the device more effective. Try using the box at night as well as during the daylight hours, with a waterproof flashlight (or an ordinary flashlight in a glass jar) as a light source.

Temperature-measuring equipment

Here is an easy-to-make device that will allow you to measure the water temperature at any desired depth. Simply lower the bottle to the required depth, pull out the stopper, and, when the bottle has filled, haul it up and read the temperature on the thermometer.

Bottom sampler

A simple dredge for obtaining samples of the pond's bottom material can be made by bolting a No. 10 can—the size used for fruit juices—to a broom handle or other pole. Flatten the mouth of the can somewhat, and punch holes in its bottom so excess water can drain off. Use the device with the same sort of motion you would use for raking leaves. Dump the bottom sample into your collecting pan or sorting screen for further processing.

Turtle traps

Turtles are among the wariest of pond animals, but you can sometimes capture them by nailing a bushel basket or similar container to the side of a favorite basking log. Your sudden appearance on the side of the pond away from the trap may startle one of the shy animals into tumbling into the basket.

Homemade Ponds

There are so many joys in having a small body of water for your very own, and so much to learn from it, that you should think seriously about the possibilities of creating one. A birdbath in a city yard is a pond and usually a good one. Birds making use of it bring cysts, spores, seeds, eggs, and microorganisms on their feet from other, distant bodies of water. Soon the water is swarming with a teeming plankton community in miniature. Even a large plastic washbasin left out and kept filled will after a while contain organisms that arrive by means of airborne spores and cysts. Flying aquatic insects—beetles, water boatmen, midges, and many others—may be attracted to the water's reflective surface.

As a slightly more ambitious project, you might consider creating a pond by excavating a pit in your backyard and placing in it a somewhat larger container—a plastic wading pool, for example—flush with the ground. If possible, select a site that gets some direct sunshine and some shade during the course of the day: too much sun can lead to overheating problems and algae population explosions.

This type of created pond lends itself well to study and observation for two reasons. First, you have more or less complete control over its contents and physical makeup, something you could not possibly achieve with a full-sized pond. Second, and more important, you have the advantage of being able to watch its ecological succession right from the very beginning, and a fascinating story will unfold as your pond develops and gradually takes on its own unique personality.

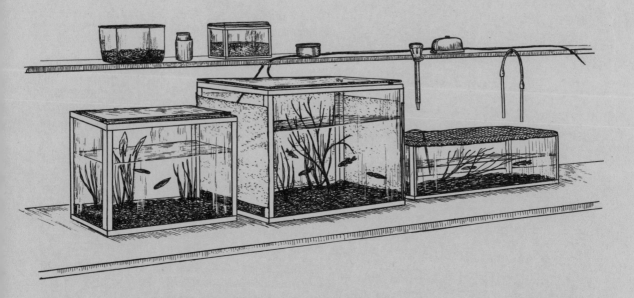

Indoor artificial ponds offer interesting projects, too. An ordinary aquarium—or better still, several aquariums—filled with pond water, a little mud and detritus from the bottom, a few selected small animals from your local pond, and some submergent plants can provide a source of year-round interest. If a sheet of glass is kept on top of the aquarium, with only a slight airspace, evaporation will be kept to a minimum and flying forms cannot escape. As you watch this miniature world month after month, you will notice patterns and cycles in the appearance of plant and animal forms.

The effectiveness of your indoor ponds will be enhanced if you observe a few simple rules. Do not add too much mud and detritus: roughly eighty percent of the aquarium's contents should be water. Direct sunlight is not necessary for the aquarium; the light from a north window is ideal. If the water becomes green too quickly with algae, cut down the light by masking the side of the aquarium toward the window with paint or paper. Most pond organisms thrive best in fairly cool waters, seventy degrees or less. Aeration is helpful but not necessary, and can be provided by an inexpensive diaphragm-type air pump of the sort used by tropical fish fanciers. Do not crowd too many animals into one tank or mix species that are not compatible. Other containers besides aquariums can be pressed into service; jars and jugs of all sizes can be set up as pond habitats.

Some naturalists have maintained such miniature ponds for years. They are far more instructive than a crystal-clear tank filled with gaudy tropical fish.

Keeping Pond Animals in the Home

A wide variety of pond animals, both large and small, can be maintained in captivity with a minimum of care and equipment. Keeping such creatures in your home, under conditions approximating their natural habitat, will give you the opportunity of studying them at close range and in detail. Given adequate care and feeding, many will carry out their complete life histories in captivity.

Before the specific needs of a few representative animals are discussed, some points of what might be called "pond watcher's etiquette" should be mentioned. First, you should never bring home more animals than you can properly care for. If you decide to maintain an animal in captivity, learn all you can about its needs and satisfy them to the best of your ability. If you cannot do so, or if your curiosity about the animal has been satisfied, release it in the same place you captured it. Occasionally you may encounter an individual animal that, for no observable reason, does not respond to home care—a turtle, for example, that simply refuses to eat. These uncooperative individuals should be released, too.

As to what animals to keep, your choice is nearly unlimited. Pond snails are among the least demanding of all, yet they are interesting creatures to observe. The common species require only a quart jar of pond water for a home and a supply of lettuce for food. Given these, they will soon deposit gelatinous egg masses on the glass. The development of the embryos within the eggs is fascinating to follow with a hand lens.

Crayfish are hardy in captivity, and thrive on a diet of aquatic vegetation and chopped meat, fish, and earthworms. Take care not to overfeed, because the unconsumed food will quickly pollute the water. Provide the tank with a few rocks under which the animals can hide. As the crayfish grow, you will get a chance to see them molt their outgrown external skeletons.

Pond leeches are easy to keep, requiring only a weekly feeding on a piece of raw liver, which should be removed from the water as soon as the leeches have had their fill. Leeches are sensitive to light, vibrations, and the presence of food juices and other chemicals in the water. You can devise simple experiments to test their reactions to these stimuli.

The nymphs of dragonflies and damselflies are interesting to observe. Fierce carnivores, they should be liberally supplied with worms, insects, and other live prey. Furnish their quarters with a stem extending up out of the water, and you may be lucky enough to witness a nymph cast its final molt and emerge as an adult.

Diving beetles, giant water bugs, backswimmers, and water boatmen are worth keeping to observe their different modes of swimming and breathing underwater. Keep their containers covered or they will fly away!

Any of the small species of pond fish are worth a try in cool, well-planted aquariums. Sticklebacks are too scrappy to be housed with other species, but their breeding behavior is so interesting that they deserve a tank to themselves. Native fishes do well on the better foods sold for tropical fishes, such as frozen adult brine shrimp, frozen daphnia, and freeze-dried *Tubifex*. The dry powdered fish foods are not satisfactory.

Because of their remarkable life histories, tadpoles are well worth your attention. If you can, collect the egg masses in the early spring and follow their development all the way through to the adult. Tadpoles are heavy eaters and need a diet of algae, canned spinach, or boiled lettuce, occasionally supplemented with a little lean raw meat. The adult frogs or toads require rather specialized care, and are best released.

Among the salamanders, the common newts make fine aquarium inhabitants. Less retiring than most of their relatives, they eagerly snap up tiny bits of meat or earthworm dangled in front of their noses on the end of a thin wire or broom straw.

Of all the pets available commercially, probably none receives as much ill treatment as the millions of baby turtles sold every

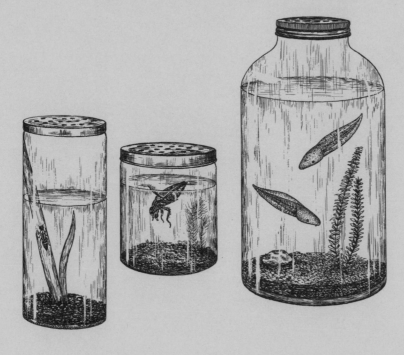

year. Given adequate care, turtles (whether you buy them in a store or catch them yourself) make hardy pets and can grow to considerable size in captivity. The basic requirements are a roomy container with enough clean water for the turtles to submerge completely, and a rock or other object that will allow them to leave the water and bask in the sun or under an electric lamp. Turtles can be fed chopped raw fish, crushed snails, and chopped earthworms. Once a week add a few drops of cod-liver oil to their food. Make sure you buy the plain, unflavored kind. A fifty-cent bottle will last you for years. Some turtles are partly or wholly herbivorous, or become so as they grow older. They should be provided with a more or less constant supply of limp lettuce leaves or other vegetable matter.

The suggestions above are necessarily brief and fragmentary; again, the important thing is to learn all you can about your captives and give them the best care possible. A small collection of well-kept animals is superior to a large collection of sick and dying ones.

Exploring the Microscopic Pond World

The possession of a microscope will quite literally open up an entire new world for you in your explorations of the pond. Each time you place a drop of pond water on a slide and bring it into focus under the microscope, you are venturing into a new; strange, and exciting world. It is an experience that no one ever tires of, no matter how many times he repeats it.

Obviously, the selection of so complicated and specialized an instrument as a microscope poses problems for the novice. If you are contemplating such a purchase, try to seek the assistance of an experienced person—a local science teacher, perhaps, or an established microscope hobbyist. Some of the things to look for—and to look out for—are discussed in the following paragraphs.

Unless your funds are fairly unlimited, you will have to make a choice between an inexpensive new instrument and an older used one. In the first group—microscopes that sell for around fifty dollars or less—the range of quality is from adequate to utterly worthless.

It is possible, for example, to buy for less than twenty dollars a hobby microscope capable of magnifying an object twelve hundred times. A professional instrument that can give good performance in that range of magnification costs between five hundred and fifteen hundred dollars. Something is clearly wrong somewhere. In fact, the combination of a low price tag and high magnification is a sure indication that the instrument is simply a waste of money.

On the other hand, the combination of low price and *low* magnification is usually an encouraging sign. A fifty-dollar microscope probably should not magnify more than two hundred times. This magnification is quite adequate for most pond work; indeed, a great deal of your work will be done at magnifications of from twenty-five to one hundred times.

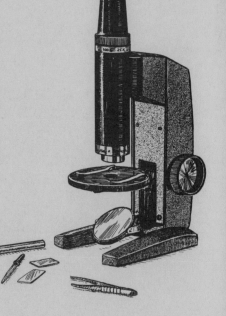

If you live in or near a large city, you might consider purchasing a used microscope; check the classified telephone directory for sources. Properly cared for, a good microscope never wears out, and very fine instruments thirty or more years old are available and are capable of giving excellent service. Prices start at around seventy-five dollars and go up, depending on the age and features of the instrument. Again, bear in mind that for pond work you will not need very high magnification. Try to buy your microscope from a reputable company that offers a guarantee on the instruments it sells.

Whether you settle upon a new microscope or a used one, by all means give it a thorough tryout before you make the purchase. It should yield a flat, crisp image, free of color fringing and distortion. Even at top magnification the image should be bright. All lens surfaces must be in perfect condition and free of chips or scratches. The focusing mechanism should work smoothly and produce a razor-sharp image. All moving parts should have a tight feel to them. A diaphragm to regulate the amount of light entering the microscope is a very desirable feature. A substage condenser is nice to have but not necessary. If you are buying a used microscope, try to avoid one equipped with an oil-immersion objective. This adds a good deal to the cost but little to the usefulness of the instrument for amateur work.

Once you have acquired your microscope, read at least one good book directed to the beginning microscopist. Remember that learning to use a microscope is something like learning to drive a car: it is wise to proceed cautiously and take one thing at a time. A good microscope, even a simple, inexpensive one, is a lifetime investment in one of the most absorbing of all pastimes.

220

An Invitation to Adventure

The foregoing pages have described a few of the multitude of activities open to the person with enough curiosity to seek out a pond and try to puzzle out some of the many riddles it poses. If you are that kind of person, many questions will probably occur to you as you begin to explore your pond, and you will go to books on aquatic biology for the answers. You may be surprised to find out that many of your questions do not yet have answers.

Even so small and commonplace a habitat as a pond contains vast realms not yet explored by science. If you are so inclined, there is no reason why you should not undertake to explore some part of this unknown territory yourself. You may make no momentous discovery, and your findings may never appear in a professional journal, but if you possess patience, the ability to work in an orderly fashion, and an active, consuming curiosity, you stand an excellent chance of making a contribution, however small, to the sum total of our knowledge of the life of ponds. And apart from the possibility of furthering science, you are certain to find an inexhaustible source of personal satisfaction and enrichment.

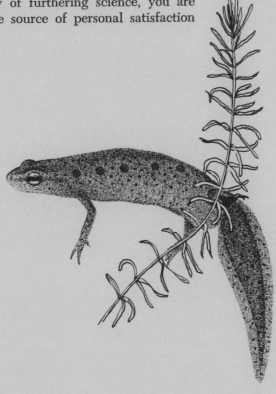

Glossary

Adaptation: An inherited characteristic that improves an organism's chances for survival in a particular *habitat*.

Algae (singular *alga*): The simplest of all green plant forms, having neither roots, stems, nor leaves.

Amphibian: Any of a group of animals that includes frogs, toads, and salamanders. Amphibians have soft, moist skins and are characterized by life cycles in which the *larvae* usually live in water and breathe through *gills*, whereas the adults live on land and breathe with *lungs* but return to the water for *spawning*.

Amphipods: A group of small *crustaceans* with bodies compressed from side to side and legs that can be used both for swimming and walking.

Antenna (plural *antennae*): A feeler; an appendage, usually (but not always) sensory in function, that occurs in pairs on the heads of *crustaceans*, insects, and certain other animals.

Aquatic: Living in fresh water, as opposed to marine. *See also* Terrestrial.

Arthropods: Animals with jointed legs and hard external skeletons. The group includes insects, *crustaceans*, spiders, mites, and other similar organisms.

Bacteria (singular *bacterium*): Simple, colorless one-celled plants, most of which are unable to manufacture their own food. Certain bacteria are of importance in the pond as *decomposers*.

Barbels: Fleshy threadlike sensory structures hanging like whiskers near the mouths of certain fishes, such as the catfish.

Benthos: Plants and animals that inhabit the bottom of the pond.

Bivalve: An animal possessing a two-part hinged shell. The fresh-water clam is a bivalve. *See also* Univalve.

Carnivore: A *predatory* animal that lives by eating the flesh of other animals. *See also* Herbivore; Omnivore.

Carrion: Dead animal remains, a source of food for *scavengers*.

Chlorophyll: A group of pigments that produces the green color of plants; essential to *photosynthesis*.

Chloroplast: A *chlorophyll*-bearing body within a plant cell in which *photosynthesis* takes place.

Cilia (singular *cilium*): Minute hairlike structures serving many purposes in a variety of animal groups. Among the *ciliates*, cilia are used for locomotion.

Ciliate: A single-celled organism that swims by means of coordinated movements of *cilia*.

Cladocerans: A group of small *crustaceans*, the water fleas, which have a pair of large Y-shaped swimming appendages.

Coelenterates: A group of simple animals, mostly marine, but represented in ponds by the hydras and the fresh-water jellyfish.

Commensalism: A relationship between two dissimilar organisms, perhaps benefiting both but not essential to the welfare of either. *See also* Mutualism.

Community: All the plants and animals in a *habitat* that are bound together by *food chains* and other relationships.

Consumer: Any living thing that is unable to manufacture food from nonliving substances, but depends instead on the energy stored in other living things. *See also* Decomposers; Predator; Primary producers.

Copepods: A group of minute *crustaceans* that have rounded bodies and a pair of elongated oarlike swimming appendages.

Crustacean: A member of a large group of animals that includes the *copepods, cladocerans, amphipods, ostracods*, and similar organisms. Crustaceans are characterized by more than four pairs of jointed legs, segmented bodies, and hard external skeletons.

Decomposers: Organisms, chiefly *bacteria* and *fungi*, that live by extracting nutrients and energy from the decaying tissues of dead plants and animals. In the process, they release chemical compounds stored in the dead bodies and make them available for use by *photosynthetic* plants.

Detritus: Minute particles of the decaying remains of dead plants and animals; an important source of food for many pond animals.

Diatom: A single-celled *alga* encased in an intricately etched pair of silica shells that fit together like a box and its lid.

Dinoflagellates: A group of one-celled organisms that possess characteristics of both plants and animals. Like plants, dinoflagellates can manufacture food through *photosynthesis*; like animals, some are capable of swimming and of catching prey.

Diurnal: Active during the daylight hours. *See also* Nocturnal.

Drought: A prolonged period when little or no precipitation falls on an area.

Ecological niche: An organism's role in a natural *community*, such as *scavenger* or *primary producer*. The term refers to function, not to the place where the organism is found.

Ecology: The scientific study of the relationships of living things to one another and to their *environment*. The scientist who studies these relationships is an ecologist.

Ecotone: An area of transition between one type of *habitat* and another.

Egg: A female reproductive cell. *See also* Fertilization.

Embryo: A developing individual before its birth or hatching.

Emergents: Plants, such as cattails and bulrushes, that root in the mud underwater and protrude above the surface. *See also* Floaters; Submergents.

Energy cycle: The process through which energy from the sun is passed from one living organism to another. Green plants, the *primary producers*, capture solar energy through *photosynthesis*. It is passed on to *herbivores*, then to one or more levels of *carnivores*, and finally to the *decomposers*, with a great deal of energy lost at each step.

Environment: All the external conditions surrounding a living thing.

Estivation: A prolonged dormant or sleeplike state that enables an animal to escape the rigors of hot, dry weather. As in *hibernation*, body processes such as breathing and heartbeat slow down drastically, and the animal neither eats nor drinks.

Estuary: A tidal river; the portion of a river that is affected by the rise and fall of the tide and that contains a graded mixture of fresh and salt water.

Evolution: The process of natural consecutive modification in the inherited makeup of living things; the process by which modern plants and animals have arisen from forms that lived in the past.

Fertilization: The union of a male reproductive cell (*sperm*) with a female reproductive cell (*egg*).

223

Filter feeder: An animal equipped with special body adaptations for straining *plankton* or minute particles of *detritus* from the water.

Flagellate: A single-celled organism that swims by means of one or more *flagella*.

Flagellum (plural *flagella*): A whiplike structure used for locomotion by a group of organisms called *flagellates*.

Floaters: Plants whose leaves float on the surface of the water. Some floaters, such as water lilies, are connected by leafstalks or stems to roots in the pond bottom. Others, such as duckweed, are not so attached, and the entire plant floats. *See also* Emergents; Neuston; Submergents.

Food chain: A series of plants and animals linked by their food relationships. *Plankton*, a plankton-eating *crustacean*, and a crustacean-eating fish would form a simple food chain. Any one species is normally represented in many food chains. *See also* Food web.

Food web: An interrelating system of *food chains*. Since few animals rely on a single source of food and because no food source is consumed by only one species of animal, the separate food chains in a natural *community* such as a pond interlock to form a food web.

Fungi (singular *fungus*): A group of plants lacking *chlorophyll*, roots, stems, and leaves. Some fungi are of importance in the pond as *decomposers*.

Gill: An organ for breathing underwater. Oxygen dissolved in the water passes through the gill membrane into the blood, while carbon dioxide passes from the blood into the water. Among the *aquatic* insects, gills serve as a medium of exchange between the water and the *tracheal system*, rather than the blood. *See also* Lung.

Habitat: The immediate surroundings (living place) of a plant or animal.

Hemoglobin: A complex pigment that imparts the red color to blood and functions as a carrier of oxygen in the blood stream.

Herbivore: An animal (also known as a first-order consumer) that eats plants, thus making the energy stored in plants available to *carnivores. See also* Omnivore.

Hibernation: A prolonged dormant or sleep-like state that enables an animal to survive during the winter months in a cold climate. The heartbeat, breathing, and other body processes of the hibernating animal slow down drastically, and it neither eats nor drinks. *See also* Estivation.

Hormone: A chemical substance produced by a living thing and used to regulate the functioning of body processes.

Host: A living organism whose body supplies food or living space for another organism. *See also* Parasite.

Incomplete metamorphosis: The type of life history, characteristic of certain insects such as the dragonflies and true bugs, in which there is no *pupal* stage. Instead, the immature insect, or *nymph*, undergoes a series of gradual changes to transform into the adult. *See also* Larva; Metamorphosis.

Invertebrate: An animal without a backbone, such as a worm, insect, *crustacean*, mollusk, and other forms, which comprise the bulk of the animal kingdom. *See also* Vertebrate.

Larva (plural *larvae*): An active immature stage in an animal's life history, during which its form differs from that of the adult, such as the "wriggler" stage in the development of a mosquito or the tadpole stage in the development of a frog. *See also* Metamorphosis; Pupa.

Limnetic zone: The open-water region of the pond, beyond the *littoral zone*.

Littoral zone: The region of the pond extending from the shore outward to the point at which most plants no longer grow.

Lung: A breathing organ consisting of air sacs lined with moist membranes permeated by minute blood vessels. Oxygen from the air passes through the membranes into the blood, while carbon dioxide passes from the blood into the air. *See also* Gill.

Metabolism: The sum of the chemical activities taking place in the cells of a living organism.

Metamorphosis: A change in the form of a living thing as it matures, especially the transformation from a *larva* to an adult. *See also* Incomplete metamorphosis; Nymph; Pupa.

Molt: To shed a body covering, such as the external skeleton of an insect or *crustacean*.

Motile: Capable of free movement. *See also* Sessile.

Mutualism: A relationship between two dissimilar organisms, benefiting both to the extent that neither lives successfully without the other. *See also* Commensalism.

Nekton: *Limnetic* organisms capable of active swimming, such as the fishes and the turtles. *See also* Plankton.

Neuston: Plants and animals that inhabit the surface of the pond, either beneath or on top of the film itself.

Nocturnal: Active at night. *See also* Diurnal.

Nymph: The immature, preadult form of certain insects, such as the dragonflies, whose life histories are characterized by *incomplete metamorphosis*. *See also* Larva; Metamorphosis.

Omnivore: An animal that eats both plants and other animals. *See also* Carnivore; Herbivore.

Organic: Pertaining to anything that is or ever was alive or produced by a plant or animal.

Ostracods: A group of small *crustaceans* characterized by clamlike *bivalve* shells.

Parasite: A plant or animal that lives on or in another organism, its *host,* and obtains shelter and food from the host's body.

Phoresis: An accidental association between two dissimilar organisms, with possible benefit to one. *See also* Commensalism; Mutualism; Symbiosis.

Photosynthesis: The process by which green plants convert carbon dioxide and water into simple sugar and free oxygen. *Chlorophyll* and sunlight are essential to the series of complex chemical reactions involved.

Phytoplankton: Plant *plankton*. *See also* Zooplankton.

Plankton: The microscopic and near-microscopic plants (*phytoplankton*) and animals (*zooplankton*) that passively drift or float in the *limnetic zone*. *See also* Nekton.

Plankton bloom: An explosive increase in the plankton population, resulting from a sudden improvement in growing conditions, such as an increase in available sunlight and nutrients.

Predator: An animal that lives by capturing other animals for food.

Primary producers: *Photosynthetic* plants, which manufacture the food on which all other living things ultimately depend. *See also* Consumer.

Production pyramid: The diminishing amount of organic material present at each successive level along a *food chain*. The decline results mainly from the constant loss of energy through *metabolism* along the food chain. *See also* Pyramid of numbers.

Protista: A term embracing all one-celled organisms, whether plant or animal—the *protozoans*, the *algae*, and the *bacteria*.

Protozoan: A simple, one-celled animal such as *Amoeba* or *Stentor*.

Pupa (plural *pupae*): The relatively inactive stage in certain insects, such as the mosquitoes and midges, during which a *larva* undergoes *metamorphosis* into an adult form. *See also* Incomplete metamorphosis.

Pyramid of numbers: The normally declining number of individuals at each successive level on a *food chain*. *See also* Production pyramid.

Scavenger: An animal that eats the dead remains and wastes of other animals and plants. *See also* Predator.

Sessile: Permanently attached to a surface; sedentary. *See also* Motile.

Sexual reproduction: Formation of a new generation through the union of female germ cells (*eggs*) and male germ cells (*sperms*). *See also* Fertilization.

Spawn: To shed reproductive cells. The term refers to animals, such as fishes, that shed *eggs* and *sperm* directly into the water.

Sperm: A male reproductive cell. *See also* Fertilization.

Spiracle: An opening for breathing, such as the external opening to an insect's *tracheal system* or the opening through which a tadpole expels water as it breathes.

Stomate: A microscopic opening in the surface of a leaf that allows gases to pass in and out.

Submergents: Plants, such as wild celery and water milfoil, which grow wholly underwater. *See also* Emergents; Floaters.

Succession: The gradual replacement of one *community* by another.

Surface tension: A property of liquids that causes the surface of a liquid to act as an elastic film. Surface tension results because molecules of liquid have a stronger attraction for each other than they do for the air molecules above them.

Symbiosis: An association of two dissimilar organisms in a relationship that may benefit one, both, or neither. *See also* Commensalism; Mutualism; Parasite; Phoresis.

Terrestrial: Living on land. *See also* Aquatic.

Territory: An area defended by an animal against others of the same species. It is used for breeding, feeding, or both.

Tracheal system: In insects and certain of their relatives, a system of minute branching air tubes called tracheae (singular *trachea*) that distributes air throughout the body, bringing in oxygen and carrying away carbon dioxide. *See also* Spiracle.

Univalve: Possessing a single, unhinged shell. Snails and limpets are univalve. *See also* Bivalve.

Vertebrate: An animal with a backbone protecting a nerve cord. The vertebrates comprise fishes, *amphibians*, reptiles, birds, and mammals. *See also* Invertebrate.

Zooplankton: Animal *plankton*. *See also* Phytoplankton.

Bibliography

FRESH-WATER BIOLOGY

BENNETT, G. W. *Management of Artificial Lakes and Ponds.* Reinhold, 1962.

BROWN, E. S. *Life in Fresh Water.* Oxford University Press, 1955.

COKER, ROBERT E. *Streams, Lakes, Ponds.* University of North Carolina Press, 1954.

EDMONDSON, W. T. (Editor). *Freshwater Biology.* Wiley, 1965.

KLOTS, ELSIE B. *The New Field Book of Freshwater Life.* Putnam, 1966.

MACAN, THOMAS T. *Freshwater Ecology.* Wiley, 1963.

MACAN, THOMAS T., and E. B. WORTHINGTON. *Life in Lakes and Rivers.* Collins, 1951.

MORGAN, ANN HAVEN. *Field Book of Ponds and Streams.* Putnam, 1930.

NEEDHAM, JAMES G., and J. T. LLOYD. *Life of Inland Waters.* Comstock, 1916.

NEEDHAM, JAMES G., and PAUL R. NEEDHAM. *A Guide to the Study of Fresh-water Biology.* Holden-Day, 1962.

POPHAM, EDWARD J. *Some Aspects of Life in Fresh Water.* Harvard University Press, 1961.

RUTTNER, FRANZ. *Fundamentals of Limnology.* University of Toronto Press, 1963.

WELCH, PAUL S. *Limnology.* McGraw-Hill, 1952.

ANIMAL LIFE

BARNES, ROBERT D. *Invertebrate Zoology.* Saunders, 1963.

CARR, A. *Handbook of Turtles.* Comstock, 1963.

CARTHY, J. D. *Animal Navigation.* Scribner, 1956.

CHU, HUNG-FU. *How to Know the Immature Insects.* William C. Brown, 1949.

CONANT, ROGER. *A Field Guide to Reptiles and Amphibians of Eastern North America.* Houghton Mifflin, 1958.

CORBET, PHILIP S. *A Biology of Dragonflies.* Quadrangle Books, 1963.

CURTIS, BRIAN. *The Life Story of the Fish.* Dover, 1949.

DOWDESWELL, W. H. *Animal Ecology.* Harper & Row, 1961.

EDDY, S. *How to Know the Freshwater Fishes.* William C. Brown, 1957.

FRAENKEL, GOTTFRIED S., and DONALD L. GUNN. *The Orientation of Animals.* Dover, 1961.

GRAY, JAMES. *How Animals Move.* Penguin, 1959.

HERALD, E. S. *Living Fishes of the World.* Doubleday, 1965.

HYLANDER, CLARENCE J. *Fishes and Their Ways.* Macmillan, 1964.

JAHN, T. L. *How to Know the Protozoa.* William C. Brown, 1949.

JAQUES, H. E. *How to Know the Insects.* William C. Brown, 1947.

LUTZ, FRANK E. *Field Book of Insects.* Putnam, 1935.

NEEDHAM, JAMES G. *Culture Methods for Invertebrate Animals.* Dover, 1937.

PENNAK, ROBERT W. *Fresh-water Invertebrates of the United States.* Ronald Press, 1953.

PETERSON, ROGER TORY. *A Field Guide to the Birds.* Houghton Mifflin, 1947.

POUGH, RICHARD H. *Audubon Water Bird Guide.* Doubleday, 1951.

ROMER, ALFRED S. *The Vertebrate Story.* University of Chicago Press, 1962.

STEBBINS, ROBERT C. *Amphibians and Reptiles of Western North America.* McGraw-Hill, 1954.

USINGER, ROBERT L. (Editor). *Aquatic Insects of California.* University of California Press, 1956.

WIGGLESWORTH, V. B. *Principles of Insect Physiology.* Dutton, 1965.

WRIGHT, ALBERT H., and ANNA A. WRIGHT. *Handbook of Frogs and Toads of the United States and Canada.* Comstock, 1933.

PLANT LIFE

BOLD, H. C. *The Plant Kingdom.* Prentice-Hall, 1965.

FAIRBROTHERS, DAVID E., and others. *Aquatic Vegetation of New Jersey.* Rutgers Extension Bulletin No. 382.

FASSETT, NORMAN C. *Manual of Aquatic Plants.* University of Wisconsin Press, 1957.

HOTCHKISS, NEIL. *Pondweeds and Pondweedlike Plants of Eastern North America.* U.S. Department of the Interior, 1964.

MUENSCHER, W. C. *Aquatic Plants of the United States.* Comstock, 1944.

PRESCOTT, G. W. *How to Know the Fresh Water Algae.* William C. Brown, 1964.

ECOLOGY

BENTON, ALLEN H., and WILLIAM E. WERNER, JR. *Field Biology and Ecology.* McGraw-Hill, 1966.

BUCHSBAUM, RALPH, and MILDRED BUCHSBAUM. *Basic Ecology.* Boxwood Press, 1957.

ODUM, EUGENE P. *Ecology.* Holt, Rinehart and Winston, 1963.

ODUM, EUGENE P., and HOWARD T. ODUM. *Fundamentals of Ecology.* Saunders, 1959.

GENERAL READING

BROWN, VINSON. *The Amateur Naturalist's Handbook.* Little, Brown, 1948.

CARRIGHAR, SALLY. *One Day at Teton Marsh.* Knopf, 1947.

DE BEER, G. *Atlas of Evolution.* Nelson, 1964.

DOBELL, CLIFFORD. *Antony van Leeuwenhoek and His "Little Animals."* Russell & Russell, 1958.

PALMER, E. LAURENCE. *Fieldbook of Natural History.* McGraw-Hill, 1949.

SIMPSON, GEORGE GAYLORD, and WILLIAM S. BECK. *Life: An Introduction to Biology.* Harcourt, Brace & World, 1965.

Illustration Credits and Acknowledgments

COVER: Young bullfrog, George Porter, National Audubon Society

ENDPAPERS: Lily pads, Josef Muench

UNCAPTIONED PHOTOGRAPHS: 8–9: Underwater scenic, B. B. Jones 56–57: Spring, William H. Amos 98–99: Backswimmer, William H. Amos 160–161: Frog in watermeal and duckweed, Edward S. Ross

ALL OTHER ILLUSTRATIONS: 10–11: William H. Amos 12: Verna R. Johnston; Durward L. Allen 13: Bob Clemenz 14: Thomas B. Hollyman, Photo Researchers 15–16: M. Woodbridge Williams 17: Michael Roberts, F.P.G. 18–19: Willis Peterson 20–21: Charles Fracé 22–23: William H. Amos 24: Hans Zillessen, Graphic Arts International 25: Mark Binn 26–27: Hans Zillessen, Graphic Arts International 28: Mark Binn 29: William H. Amos 30: Laurence Lowry 31: Grant Heilman 32–35: Hans Zillessen, Graphic Arts International 36: M. Woodbridge Williams, National Park Service 37: William H. Amos 38–39: Glenn D. Chambers 40: Grant Haist 41: William H. Amos 42: Treat Davidson, National Audubon Society (perch); William H. Amos (shiner) 43: Treat Davidson, National Audubon Society (bass, bullhead) 44: William H. Amos 45: J. M. Conrader; William H. Amos 46: Patricia C. Henrichs 47: B. B. Jones 48: William H. Amos 49: L. R. Owen; William H. Amos 50–51: William H. Amos 52–53: Hans Zillessen, Graphic Arts International 54: William H. Amos 58: Grant Haist 59: Bob and Ira Spring 60–61: Donald J. Waters 62: Patricia C. Henrichs 63: Norman R. Lightfoot 64: Robert Leatherman 65: Mark Binn (after Corbet) 66: Patricia C. Henrichs 67: W. V. Crich 68: William J. Jahoda; William H. Amos 69: B. B. Jones; William H. Amos 70–71: William H. Amos 72: Charles Fracé 73: William J. Bolte 74: Norman R. Lightfoot 75: Thase Daniel 76–78: William H. Amos 80: Bill Reasons 81: Patricia C. Henrichs 82–83: Mark Binn 84: Jack Dermid; Kelly Motherspaugh 85: Thase Daniel 86–87: Norman Cousins 88: Patricia C. Henrichs 90–93: Laurence Pringle 94: William H. Amos 95: Mark Binn (after Welch) 96: Bill Ratcliffe 100–101: Hans Zillessen, Graphic Arts International 102–103: Patricia C. Henrichs 104: Douglas Faulkner 107: William H. Amos 108: Lynwood Chase 109: Douglass Hubbard 110: Charles Fracé 111: William H. Amos 112: Jack Dermid 113: Thase Daniel; William H. Amos 114–115: Patricia C. Henrichs 116: Mark Binn 117–121: William H. Amos 122: Hans Zillessen, Graphic Arts International 124–126: William H. Amos 127: Mark Binn (after Popham) 128: Patricia C. Henrichs (after Pennak and Townsend) 129: Allan Roberts 130: Hans Zillessen, Graphic Arts International; William H. Amos 131: Mark Binn (after Lois and Louis Darling) 132–133: Allan Roberts 134: Harry Engels 135: Willis Peterson 136–137: William J. Bolte 139: F.P.G. 140: Matthew Vinciguerra 141: William H. Amos 142: Allan Roberts 143: Allan Roberts; Shelly Grossman, F.P.G. 144: Shelly Grossman, F.P.G. 145: Elgin Ciampi 146: William H. Amos 147: Charles Fracé; William H. Amos 148: Larry West, Full Moon Studio 149: Patricia C. Henrichs 150–151: Charles Fracé 152–154: William H. Amos 155: Hans Zillessen, Graphic Arts International 156: Edward S. Ross 157: William H. Amos; Mark Binn (after Carthy) 158: William H. Amos 160–161: Edward S. Ross 162: Anton van Leeuwenhoek 163: William H. Amos 164: Patricia C. Henrichs; William H. Amos 165–167: William H. Amos 168: William Taylor 169–171: Charles Fracé 172: William H. Amos 173: Patricia C. Henrichs 174: Mark Binn 175: William H. Amos 176: Patricia C. Henrichs; Edward S. Ross 177: Edward S. Ross 178–179: Charles Fracé 180: William H. Amos; Mark Binn 182–183: William H. Amos 184: Patricia C. Henrichs 185: Hugh Spencer 186–189: William H. Amos 190: Carl Struwe, Monkmeyer Press Photos 191: Patricia C. Henrichs 192–193: William H. Amos 194: B. B. Jones; William H. Amos 195–198: William H. Amos 201–221: Charles Fracé

PHOTO EDITOR: ROBERT J. WOODWARD

AUTHOR'S ACKNOWLEDGMENT: *A book of this sort is a compendium from many sources, including books, journals, and my colleagues at the University of Delaware and elsewhere. My wife and children have been with me on countless trips to ponds throughout the country. But it is perhaps to my students that I owe the greatest debt of gratitude, for they have worked with me for twenty years on local ponds and have opened my eyes to much that I could not have otherwise seen.*

The publisher also wishes to thank F. C. Gillette, former Chief, Division of Wildlife Refuges; C. Gordon Fredine, Chief, Division of International Affairs of the National Park Service; and the park superintendents and refuge managers who responded in detail to a questionnaire on ponds in areas administered by the Department of the Interior. The publisher also expresses appreciation to William Perry, O. L. Wallis, and M. Woodbridge Williams of the National Park Service for their assistance in reading the manuscript or locating photographs. Finally, the publisher gratefully acknowledges permission to reprint the passage on page 161 from Clifford Dobell (Ed. and Transl.), Antony van Leeuwenhoek and His "Little Animals," Russell & Russell, New York, 1958.

Index

[Page numbers in **boldface** type indicate reference to illustrations and maps.]